SCOTTISH BANKNOTES

SCOTTISH BANKNOTES

James Douglas, A.I.B. (Scot.)

Stanley Gibbons Publications Ltd
391 Strand, London WC2R 0LX

By Appointment to Her Majesty The Queen
Stanley Gibbons Ltd, Philatelists

© Stanley Gibbons Publications Ltd 1975
First published 1975

ISBN 0 85259 775 4

Printed in Great Britain by
William Clowes & Sons Limited, London, Colchester and Beccles

"How seldom when we place a stamp upon a letter or 'bang' a sixpence do we think of either the stamp or the coin as a work of art, or regard as an art collection the few Bank notes of which we may gain temporary command. Yet the Bank note can be a work of art and offer, on grounds of pure aesthetics, sufficient justification for our joy in its possession. It can revive old memories and have links and associations with the past, adding a value far beyond the legend on its face."

– Stanley Curister, O.B.E., R.S.A., R.S.W., Director of the National Gallery of Scotland, quoted in *The Bank of Scotland 1695–1945*, by Charles A. Malcolm.

Preface

This is the first catalogue to embrace the entire range of Scottish banknotes from 1695 to date. The increase in interest shown by the public in bank and currency notes has prompted its publication and it has been written for the collector rather than the historian. The history of the Scottish banks has been well documented, that of the notes issued by them has not. Nevertheless the notes mirror the history of the banks and sufficient historical background has been included to enable the reader to have a proper understanding of all the factors involved.

It is a reference catalogue of "types", listing over 800 "face-different" notes of 80 banks, omitting minor variations in design. It is the result of many years of research. The collection of Scottish banknotes in the possession of the Institute of Bankers in Scotland has been used as a basis for the catalogue, but much additional information has been obtained from the reference collections of the three Scottish banks, from that of the National Museum of Antiquities of Scotland (which includes the Morgan Collection of modern notes) and from recourse to collections in private hands.

It cannot claim to include every note issued. This ideal can never be achieved as some of the notes and the records of their designs have been lost forever. Most of the information given has been obtained from perusal of the actual notes, proofs and specimens or pieced together from the all-too-rare references in banking literature and official records. Everyone interested in Scottish banknotes will find at long last in this catalogue a means of identification and classification of these interesting and attractive issues and it should prove a valuable work of reference to collectors and dealers alike. Particular attention is drawn to the valuation guide which will be found at the end of the book to which Stanley Gibbons Currency Ltd. have added actual prices.

Edinburgh   JAMES DOUGLAS

Acknowledgements

It would have been impossible to complete this work without the assistance and encouragement of:

The Secretary and Staff of the Institute of Bankers in Scotland.

The officials of the Bank of Scotland, The Royal Bank of Scotland Limited, and the Clydesdale Bank Limited.

The Keeper and Assistant Keeper of the National Museum of Antiquities of Scotland.

The author is also greatly indebted to Mr. Alistair Gibb who, in spite of his many commitments, agreed to check the manuscript. His advice and helpful comments have been of great value. Mr. Gibb will be known to many readers as a pioneer in the field of Scottish banknote collecting. For the present work he kindly lent for illustration the notes of the Bannockburn Iron Works and the Carron Company, in addition to No. 1 of the Galloway Banking Company and No. 32 of The Royal Bank of Scotland.

The courtesy of the Bank of Scotland in lending for illustration notes from the following banks is also gratefully acknowledged:

Bank of Scotland (Nos. 20 and 39); British Linen Bank (Nos. 9, 12 and 22); Caledonian Banking Company (Nos. 17 and 18); Central Bank of Scotland (Nos. 5 and 7); Sir William Forbes, James Hunter & Company (No. 4); Glasgow Union Banking Company (Nos. 1 and 2); The Kilmarnock Bank (No. 1); The Paisley Union Banking Company (No. 3); The Ship Bank (No. 1); and the Union Bank of Scotland (No. 15).

To these people and institutions the author extends his grateful thanks and appreciation for the patience and courtesy shown to him during his researches.

Contents

Index of Issuing Banks or Authorities

SCOTTISH BANKNOTES

Introduction

Although Scotland cannot claim to be the first European country to issue banknotes it is safe to say that nowhere else did paper currency contribute so much to the national economy in the eighteenth and nineteenth centuries. The reason for this is that public confidence in the banknotes was so highly sustained that a paper circulation was preferred to a metallic one. The position in England was of course quite different. Here paper money was regarded with suspicion by the public, perhaps not without just cause, and the mercantile community was saddled with a metallic currency with all its attendant inconvenience and cost. That cost was considerable when the expense of transporting large quantities of gold and silver coin from one part of the country to another was involved and this continual movement was necessary in commercial circles because of the reluctance of the public to accept other than gold and silver coin in settlement of a transaction. Certainly a very wide range of banknotes existed in England at the beginning of the nineteenth century but they found little favour among the general public. Even Bank of England notes, which at the turn of that century were for large denominations only, seldom circulated far from London. It must be realised that the English banking system of those days was vastly different from that which now exists and which has established for itself an unrivalled reputation for reliability. Then it consisted of innumerable private and local banks with relatively small resources. Scarcely a week passed without at least one of them falling by the wayside. Upwards of 500 of these banks were issuing their own notes in 1810. It is easy to understand why the average citizen preferred the inconvenience of coin to the uncertainty of paper. It is important therefore for everyone interested in Scottish banknotes to understand the reason why they were so favoured by the public north of the Tweed as this factor has a considerable bearing on the availability – or rather the non-availability – of the earlier notes to collectors.

A century and a half ago there was a basic difference in the banking systems of England and Scotland and reference has already been made to the many small private banks which existed in the former country. Scotland in contrast had developed its system along joint-stock lines, creating relatively large "public" banks with branches throughout the country, a system later to be adopted in England and one which forms the basis of present-day British banking.

The inherent strength of the Scottish banks was therefore the first factor in the creation of confidence in their issues which, by virtue of the branch system, circulated and were recognised by the public over a wide area of the country. In spite of the existence of large banks – and "large" in this context is merely a comparative term – Scotland was by no means immune from bank failures, but holders of notes of any bank which failed suffered no loss. Together with other creditors they had recourse to the assets of all the shareholders whose liability in those days was not limited, instead of to the resources of a few partners as in the case of a private bank. In the long history of Scottish banking only about three cases are recorded where the noteholders were not paid in full and in each of these cases the holders received upwards of 50 per cent of their money. Holders of notes issued by numerous private individuals and traders in the mid-eighteenth century were not always so lucky but these were not *bank*notes and more of them anon. This then was another factor contributing to the general acceptability of a Scottish banknote – it had a built-in cover against loss! An additional selling point was the custom of the Scottish banks to make full payment for any forged note presented by an innocent holder as it was important to preserve the reputation of the issue.

The comparative freedom from legislative interference enjoyed by the Scottish banks, in marked contrast to the restrictions being imposed on their English colleagues at that time, enabled the note issue to be developed in a manner dictated by public requirements. The efficient system of note exchanges set up in Scotland prevented over-issue by any particular bank as effectively as any artificial restriction could hope to do. The faith in the notes and the public's preference for paper in place of gold is best illustrated by this extract from the minutes of the Select Committee appointed under Lord Liverpool to examine the position of note issues in Scotland in 1825 and in which an eminent banker was being questioned.

"Q. Regarding gold coin, the public shows no disposition to acquire it?
A. They show the greatest disposition to get quit of it when it comes into their hands."

It was not sufficient for banknotes to be more convenient than gold, they had to be as good as gold. An appreciation of this situation can explain why so few of the older Scottish issues have survived. If forged notes and notes of banks which had failed were paid in full what inducement was there to retain specimens as souvenirs? The so-called "broken bank" notes of other countries available to collectors in quantity have no counterpart in the Scottish issues, nor also have the "cancelled" notes of English banks which appear to have leaked in profusion from the custody of the banks which absorbed them.

Collectors must face up to the fact that old Scottish notes are rare and that they may have to be content with unissued notes, proofs and "specimens", which fortunately are more readily available.

The History of the Notes

The first Scottish notes were issued in 1695 by the Bank of Scotland – the same year as the first printed issues of the Bank of England. The notes were in denominations of £5, £10, £20, £50, and £100 sterling. Notes for £1 did not appear until 1704, these being inscribed £12 Scots, the equivalent of £1 sterling. Although the Union of the Parliaments in 1707 created a unified currency through Britain the custom of quoting the value in Scottish pounds as well as in sterling continued to be a feature of banknotes for many years afterwards. The Bank of Scotland enjoying its monopoly remained the only issuing source of notes until that monopoly lapsed and the Royal Bank of Scotland entered the scene in 1727. The "New" Bank, as it was commonly referred to in order to distinguish it from the "Old" Bank, immediately issued notes and the rivalry between the two banks soon developed into a state of open war. One bank would gather together a quantity of the other's notes and by presenting them all at the one time hoped to cause as much embarrassment as possible or even because of the shortage of coin to secure a suspension of payment on the part of its rival.

A result of this type of activity was the introduction by the Bank of Scotland in 1730 of the Option Clause. This was a clause inserted on the note making it payable on demand or in the option of the directors six months after presentation with the addition of interest at the current rate. Royal Bank notes continued to be payable on demand until 1761 when they too included the Option Clause. Meantime The British Linen Company had been established in 1746 in order to foster the linen trade but it soon entered the banking field at first as a sideline. Notes were issued by them in 1747 "for value received in goods" but the first true banknotes did not appear until 1750, and it was not long before they too incorporated the Option Clause. The Option Clause was of course a retrograde step – the essential feature of a banknote being the holder's ability to exchange it for cash whenever he wanted to – and so the provisions of an Act of 1765, which declared the Clause illegal, restored the situation.

This, however, was the one period in Scottish banking history when all the worst features of a paper currency manifested themselves. It should be pointed out at this stage that in Scotland the right to issue notes was one at common law. In simple terms this meant that anyone had a right to issue notes, the only proviso being that someone was willing to accept them! In the mid-eighteenth century this right began to be exercised by traders, shopkeepers and even private individuals. This has been referred to as the period of the note-issuing mania. Some notes were issued for sums as low as 1s. Scots (1d. sterling) complete with Option Clause! Many caricatures were circulated bearing the strangest of options. None of these notes were *bank*notes and as such are not within the scope of the present work, but one issue, that of George Keller & Son, has been included in the catalogue in order to provide an example of the type. A further provision of the 1765 Act declared that no note of a lower denomination than £1 sterling should be issued and sanity was gradually restored.

Notes of this period were designed in a simple manner, the issues of the Royal Bank being perhaps more advanced technically as they incorporated a portrait of the King. The others had no vignettes and very little ornamentation, relying on the intricacy of the script for protection. Copper plates were used for the engraving. As could be expected such simple notes attracted the attention of the forger. Forgeries, however, were not prevalent and as often as not were executed by hand using pen and ink. Execution by another method awaited the perpetrator if caught! By 1790 there was a more artistic approach to the design of banknotes and the services of highly skilled engravers, notably Robert Kirkwood, were obtained. Printing was still from copper plates but the quality had improved tremendously. Vignettes increased in size, offering greater scope to both artist and engraver while at the same time providing a greater measure of security. Although the Royal Bank had experimented with colour printing by producing in 1777 the first British notes to be printed in three colours, most notes were still printed in black and were invariably uniface. The blank expanse of the back provided a fine circulating medium for slogans, etc., ranging from religious texts to ribald rhymes. The production of notes from copper plates reached its artistic peak around 1820, the Edinburgh firm of Robert Kirkwood & Son being responsible for the design and engraving of most of the issues.

The technical skill of the forger had also advanced over the years and a number of forgeries appeared at this time. These were not the crude pen-drawn or woodblock productions of earlier years but were from the same type of copper plates as the originals, some of the false engravings displaying considerable merit. A number of contemporary forgeries were the work of French prisoners of war held in camps near Edinburgh and Perth. It can be assumed that these were produced with the active cooperation of their guardians who no doubt received some form of "dividend" from the enterprise.

Forgeries of Scottish notes, although they constituted a nuisance, were not unduly prevalent. Figures supplied by the Depute Clerk of Justiciary in Edinburgh show that in the twenty years 1806–1825 there were 86 prosecutions for banknote forgery in Scotland, eight of the culprits being executed. In England during the same period there were upwards of 1,000 prosecutions, resulting in over 300 executions. The existence of the forgeries, however, put pressure on the Scottish banks to up-date their methods of security printing, an initial step being the introduction of steel plates or steel-plated copper plates. Much finer detail was possible in steel engraving and many of the notes produced during the period 1825–1860 are really works of art, the quality of the engraving being quite beyond the skill of the normal forger. The few forgeries which did appear during this period were either from copper plates or were lithographed, and their detection presented little difficulty.

The firm of W. H. Lizars sprang into prominence at this time and notes engraved on their plates were issued not only by the majority of Scottish banks but also by the banks in the north of England and the Isle of Man. The famous London firm of Perkins & Heath, later Perkins Bacon & Co., has always been associated with security printing from steel plates and indeed a few Scottish notes were printed by them, but the Lizars plates had a greater artistic appeal. The reason for this lies in the different approach of each of the two firms to the problem of security. Perkins & Heath relied on intricate geometric patterns with which to embellish the design while the Scottish firm produced a plethora of allegorical and classical figures as ornaments for their notes, Royal Portraits being also included. Which approach afforded the greater security it is impossible to say as there were so few forgeries. Among other steel-plate engravers of banknotes operating in Scotland at this time, mention must be made of W. & A. K. Johnston of Edinburgh, Joseph Swan and Gilmour & Dean of Glasgow and J. Fenton of Dundee. W. H. Lizars died in 1859 and in the following year his firm was taken over by W. & A. K. Johnston, this fact accounting for the change in the imprint on a number of former Lizars plates.

Until the mid-nineteenth century all notes were hand-signed, the earlier notes by officials but later by subordinates on their behalf. Numbers were invariably inserted by hand as also in most cases was the date. Printed dates, however, did appear from time to time on very early notes. The paper used was normally of very high quality, usually incorporating a distinctive watermark. This often consisted of the title of the bank in large letters covering the whole area of the note but some of the smaller banks were content to print on paper bearing the manufacturers' own watermark. With the advance of printing technique a number of banks dispensed with a watermark but in recent years this has been reintroduced. All current Scottish notes have fairly elaborate watermarks as intrinsic parts of the design.

Early notes were bound into books of 100 or 200 notes. Each had a counterfoil on which the number and date of issue could be recorded. Separation from the counterfoil was effected by an irregular scissors cut, often through a printed vertical panel at the left of the design. This explains why some early notes appear to have the left edge of the design incomplete. When the note was presented for payment the irregular left edge could be matched against the counterfoil, thus confirming that it was genuine.

Nineteenth Century Issues

So much then for the anatomy of the earlier notes. Apart from their physical features what other influences affected these issues? The return to sanity after the note-issuing mania of the mid-eighteenth century witnessed a steady increase in public confidence in the issues of the established banks, especially in those of the three old Chartered Banks, the Bank of Scotland, The Royal Bank of Scotland and The British Linen Company. The financial crisis at the end of the century which had a disastrous effect on English banking was not felt to the same extent in Scotland, largely due to the strength of the banks. It is recorded that during the period of inconvertibility notes of the Bank of England circulating in the north of that country fell to a discount while Scottish notes circulated in the northern counties at par. There was, however, one blot on the Scottish banking copy book at that time – the failure of Douglas Heron & Co. in 1772. This failure was due to mismanagement. Noteholders were of course paid in full as were the general creditors.

Early in the nineteenth century there emerged a number of new joint stock banks, notably the Commercial Bank and the National Bank, with head offices in Edinburgh; the Clydesdale Bank and the Union Bank in Glasgow and the Town and County Bank and North of Scotland Bank in Aberdeen. Glasgow was also the birthplace of the Western Bank and the City of Glasgow Bank of which one historian wrote "it would have been better had they died in infancy", but more of them in a later paragraph. One great danger to the Scottish note issue was narrowly averted in 1825 when Westminster politicians attempted to interfere with the established system. The chaotic condition of note issues in England at that time was the cause of much public distress and Parliament was forced to take action. The result was the Act of 1825 which did much to restore stability. Among the provisions of this Act was the prohibition of banknotes for sums under £5. It also sanctioned the creation of joint stock banks in England and persuaded the Bank of England to increase its influence in the provinces by opening a number of branches in various parts of the country. Unfortunately an attempt was made to extend some of the provisions of the Act to Scotland by politicians who displayed almost complete ignorance of the conditions existing there, where the joint stock and branch system had already been soundly established over a considerable period of time. However, it was the prospect of losing their £1 note which prompted the public to protest to such an extent that Parliament suspended further action until they had the benefit of the report of a Select Committee under Lord Liverpool appointed to look into the matter. The findings of the Committee were overwhelmingly in support of the status quo in Scotland so that the attempts to interfere were abandoned and the Scottish £1 note was reprieved.

Although the 1825 Act improved the position in England it did not effect a complete cure for the ailments of the banking system which still lacked sufficient strength to weather the recurring crises of the period. Many of the new joint stock banks were hastily conceived and badly managed. The resulting Bank Charter Act of 1844, with its Scottish counterpart of 1845, still remains the main regulator of banking within the United Kingdom to this day. The main provision of both the English and Scottish

Acts was the establishment of an Authorised Circulation for each bank of issue based on its average circulation calculated over a prescribed period of twelve months. No new banks of issue could be created. The two Acts differ in several respects, the most important concerning the Authorised Circulation. In England this figure could not be exceeded under any circumstances whereas the Scottish banks were permitted to issue in excess of the figure to the extent of the gold and silver coin held by them as "cover". Treasury and Bank of England notes replaced coin as cover in later years. It has been suggested that there was no real necessity for the Scottish Act but its effect on the note issue was not apparent to the public.

The two most momentous happenings in Scottish banking in the second half of the nineteenth century were undoubtedly the failures of the Western Bank of Scotland in 1857 and of the City of Glasgow Bank in 1878. Both failures were the result of mismanagement but while this was caused simply by the absence of a proper degree of business acumen in the case of the Western Bank, the mismanagement of the City Bank had criminal implications. Both failures were major disasters and caused great distress in business and commercial circles. The general public as depositors and noteholders did not suffer, but the shareholders, in view of their unlimited liability, certainly did. It is interesting to note that banknotes of the Western Bank, although it failed over a century and a quarter ago, will still be paid by the Royal Bank of Scotland Ltd. as successors to the National Bank of Scotland, which took over that responsibility at the time of the failure. Notes of the City of Glasgow Bank were first met by all the other Scottish banks and later by the Assets Company Ltd., which was set up to deal with outstanding assets and liabilities of the City Bank. One beneficial result of the collapse of the City Bank was the incorporation of all but the three Chartered Banks in the Companies Act of 1879 and the adoption of limited liability. This is reflected in the change of title of the banks concerned by the addition of "Limited". The three senior banks by virtue of their Charters did not require that appendage.

What of the notes themselves in the second half of the nineteenth century? Printing techniques did not change a great deal during that period, and the basic plates from which the notes were printed were virtually the same as in earlier years. The danger of forgery, however, had increased with the advance of photography and to offset this the banks began to print their notes in two or more colours. The engraved plate printed one colour and a second impression in another colour was added by a lithographic or similar process. Blue and red were frequently chosen because of the inability of the photographic emulsion of the time to render them correctly on the negative. Emulsions of the period were over-sensitive to blue and virtually non-sensitive to red. Dates and numbers were now printed on the notes instead of being inserted by hand and the introduction of a printed facsimile of at least one of the signatures on each note was a logical step in view of the constant increase in the number in circulation. The custom of signing notes by hand took a long time to die out completely, however, and survived on the £1 notes of the Royal Bank until 1935 and on the larger denominational notes until considerably later. No Scottish notes are now hand-signed. Most notes now had printed backs as an additional measure of security although uniface notes continued to be issued by the Bank of Scotland and the Royal and Clydesdale Banks until comparatively recent times.

Twentieth Century Issues

At the beginning of the twentieth century there were ten banks of issue in Scotland. The Caledonian and the Town and County soon disappeared and for almost half a century the remaining eight continued to have separate issues. Now there are only three.

Not only was the number of issuing banks reduced but commencing in 1924 the size of the notes which they issued was also progressively reduced. Scottish issues in the twentieth century were subjected to certain legal changes. At the beginning of the 1914–18 War they were made legal tender together with the new Treasury £1 and 10s. notes, but this new status made absolutely no difference in practice to their acceptance by the public. No paper money had ever been legal tender in Scotland, yet up to this time no country had enjoyed so strong or so popular a paper currency as Scotland, so the question as to whether or not the notes were legal tender was of little significance. The "status" was withdrawn after that war but restored in the 1939–45 War. Bank of England £1 and 10s. notes became legal tender in Scotland in 1928 but this was not extended to notes of higher denomination.

No Scottish bank may issue without permission the notes of another, those taken in by way of business being "cleared" at the Note Exchanges in the same manner as cheques. To assist in the task of "sorting" the notes distinctive markings in magnetic ink began to appear on the backs of the £1 notes in 1967 and this was later extended to £5 notes. In some cases the design was modified to accommodate these markings. The now familiar steel strips were also introduced about this time. A recent innovation is the issue of notes in "sets" featuring a particular theme after the style of postage stamps. The Clydesdale Bank has produced a set which can aptly be termed "Famous Scots", featuring portraits of eminent Scotsmen on the front and illustrations on the back relevant to the person portrayed. The latest issue of the Royal Bank, while having a uniform design on the front, carries a series of illustrations of Scottish castles on the back. Should this policy continue it will create a greater interest among collectors as the two issues referred to are very attractive indeed.

At present then there are three distinct bank issues in Scotland each with entirely different designs but now with each denomination in uniform colours corresponding to the notes of the Bank of England. The highest denomination is £100 (the highest denomination issued by the Bank of

England at the time of writing being £20). The total circulation of the Scottish banks amounts to over £250 million, constituting the main currency of the country. In fact the Scottish note circulation accounts for 7 per cent of the total currency of the British Isles. This figure may be seen in its proper perspective when it is realised that the population of the whole of Scotland is considerably less than that of Greater London.

Bank of England notes also circulate in Scotland, being brought there by travellers from the south – in large quantities during the tourist season – but apart from those held to cover the excess over the Authorised Circulation the remainder are quickly returned to England.

Does the right to issue afford any advantage to a Scottish bank? The answer is Yes! The enormous sums of cash required by a bank to provide till money and reserves at its branches implies a loss of earning power and interest on the amount involved – and many millions of pounds are so involved. A Scottish bank retains such sums mostly in the form of its own notes and of course until such notes are issued over the counter they constitute no liability to the bank. It is just like writing a cheque. Until the cheque is actually handed out to someone no cash has been parted with. The interest saved and the funds released for other purposes by holding cash reserves in the form of its own notes provides the bank with an earning capacity well in excess of the stamp duty, the licences and the cost of printing and maintaining the issue. The cost of licences and stamp duty was calculated at £544,000 in 1962 and no doubt has risen since then. The cost of production of the notes would be more difficult to assess. Licences to issue notes, together with the relative stamp duties, were, however, abolished in 1972.

What of the future? It would be foolish to make predictions, but if Scotland is permitted to retain its present banking system any attempt to suppress its time-honoured paper currency would be met by the same vigorous opposition which manifested itself a century and a half ago. However, if we ignore the future, the Scottish note issues present and past afford to the collector an unrivalled field of interest which for variety, beauty, and scope for study is certainly unequalled by any other British issues.

Catalogue Notes

Banks have been listed in alphabetical order irrespective of mergers or affiliations. Although this may be illogical from the historical angle it will provide readers with an easier form of reference. They should, however, familiarise themselves first with the details which follow.

NOTE SIZES

The sizes of Scottish banknotes at first sight appear as manifold as their colours and designs, but in fact the sizes fall neatly into four distinct categories for the "small" denominational notes and four for the "large" denominations. These are accorded reference letters, namely A, B, C and D for notes of £1 and £1 1s. (and occasionally of £2) and W, X, Y and Z for notes of £5 and upwards.

"Small" Denominations

	Approx. size in millimetres	Types of notes applicable
Size A	145 × 110	This is the size of the large "square" £1 notes of the pre-1927 period. Considerable variation in actual size occurs in this category, especially in the earlier notes.
Size B	140 × 75	The size of the Treasury and 1928 type Bank of England £1 notes. Adopted by the Scottish banks for £1 notes from the mid-1920s until the early 1960s.
Size C	143 × 63	Roughly similar to the present (1975) £1 Bank of England note. Used by the Scottish banks throughout the 1960s.
Size D	126 × 60	The size in current use.

"Large" Denominations

Size W	195 × 120	The size in use for notes of £5 and over in the pre-1950 period. Familiarly referred to by Scottish bank staffs of that era as "horse blankets".

Size X	170 × 93	This reduction in size occurred in the late 1940s. £20 and £100 notes continue to be issued in this size.
Size Y	150 × 82	An interim reduction which took place about 1961, but restricted to £5 notes. Retained for £10 notes which were issued a few years later.
Size Z	134 × 77	The size of the current £5 notes in Scotland.

The dimensions given should be regarded as "average" as small variations exist as between different banks and issues.

SIGNATURES ON SCOTTISH NOTES

Until about 1875 *all* Scottish notes were signed by hand either by an official or on his behalf; consequently no reference is made on the lists to the fact that such notes bear manuscript signatures. The increase in the number of notes circulating by the end of the nineteenth century necessitated the introduction of facsimile signatures, either engraved on the plate itself or printed on the note by lithography or other method. To simplify matters all such signatures are referred to as "printed" signatures.

The importance attached to signatures on modern Bank of England notes, by which means alone the various issues are distinguishable, does not apply to Scottish notes, as these are all dated. Various printings are therefore distinguished by date and not by signature. Indeed collectors are strongly urged to avoid reference to any particular Scottish note by the signature on it as by doing so they may overlook more important variations in the note types. To quote one example which will underline this point let us take the £1 note of the National Bank of Scotland Ltd. dated 2 February 1931 and printed by Waterlow & Sons Ltd. This bears the signature of the Cashier, George Drever. So also does the printing of 11 November 1932, but this is by a new printer and by a different printing method. The printing of 1 August 1935 was still signed by George Drever but the Royal Arms are now replaced by those of the Bank. All three notes appear similar at first glance and all bear a similar signature yet reliance on that as a distinguishing feature could result in the difference in the types being overlooked – and the first type is a scarce one!

Collect types by date and not by signature!

NOTES PAYABLE TO BEARER OR PAYABLE TO AN INDIVIDUAL

Some, although not all, of the earlier notes are made payable to an official of the bank (normally the Secretary) or to bearer. The reason for this was the belief held in some quarters that promissory notes required to be drawn out in favour of a named person and not merely to the bearer. The custom was discontinued in the middle of the nineteenth century. The name of the "payee" was usually inserted by hand, but where the name was actually engraved on the plate reference is made to it on the lists.

CONDITION

Obviously the aim is to include in a collection notes in uncirculated condition or as near to that state as possible. With Scottish notes this ideal may be attainable in most post-war issues but it is a virtual impossibility with the earlier issues. A realistic approach to the question of condition must therefore be adopted. Remember that most notes prior to 1853 bore either an embossed or a printed revenue stamp. Consequently they were permitted to remain in circulation so long as they held together in one piece, as when they were withdrawn the bank lost the value of the "stamp". In any case these early Scottish notes are so rare that they merit collecting in any condition!

Values quoted are therefore based on the following grades:

Prior to 1880	up to F
1881–1940	VF
1941–1965	EF
from 1965	UNC

Unissued notes, proofs and "specimen" notes are valued in EF condition.

DATES OF THE VARIOUS PRINTINGS

Variations in colour shades, etc., frequently occur in different printings of a particular type especially if it has been in issue over a long period. Although this is primarily a "type" catalogue, particulars of dates of issue of many twentieth century £1 notes have been added to assist collectors. It should be emphasised that the dates quoted are those recorded by the author and may not necessarily be complete. No special significance should therefore be attached to a note bearing a date not included in the list.

PROOFS, SPECIMENS, ESSAYS AND COLOUR TRIALS

These items are always sought after by collectors and reference to their application to Scottish banknotes may be of assistance.

Proofs

Three types of proofs are met with. In the first place we have the proof of the design as submitted by the printers to the bank for approval. This is usually printed on a plate-sunk card of considerably larger size than the design and for want of a better term may be referred to as a bank proof. Such proofs are of course extremely scarce and are seldom available to collectors.

More frequently seen are the proofs on card or paper provided to the banks for circulation to their agents in order to familiarise them with a new design. Such proofs are often endorsed "Proof Note", "Specimen" or "Cancelled", either in print or manuscript. Unissued and unsigned notes were also used for this purpose. These types of proofs are normally restricted to the nineteenth century issues, particularly those of mid-century.

The third type of proof is the production proof, consisting of "pulls" of vignettes or parts of the note although sometimes of the whole design. These were for internal use in the printing establishment or for submission to the banks in relation to some modification in the design. They are rarely seen outside the reference collections held by the banks.

Specimens

Apart from the proof notes endorsed "Specimen" referred to above, specimen notes exist for most twentieth century issues. These consist of the note in its issued form and colour overprinted "Specimen". Such notes are either without signature or number or bear the signature and a "zero" number, e.g. A 000000. They are produced in very limited quantities for use within banking circles and are no longer circulated on a large scale to agents and correspondents; photographic reproductions now suffice for that purpose. Modern specimen notes are therefore seldom seen by collectors.

Essays and Colour Trials

Essays are unadopted designs which have been submitted to the banks by security printers either by invitation or as a speculation. Printings of adopted designs in a variety of colours are sometimes also submitted before the actual "issue" colour is decided. Such essays and colour trials are of course rarely seen outside the bank reference collections.

MAGNETIC SORTING MARKS

A logical development of the electronic age of banking was the provision in 1967 of markings on the back of notes in magnetic ink which could be "read" by machines and thus enable the issues of the various banks to be sorted. No one Scottish bank is permitted to issue the notes of another and therefore the separation of notes destined for the Note Exchanges is a time-consuming activity if they are "spread" by hand. The machine can operate at a speed of 600 notes per minute. The principle adopted consists of seven small horizontal bars spaced differently for each bank. This code is repeated in inverted form to enable the machine to operate even if a note is fed to it in an upside-down position. These markings were at first restricted to £1 notes but were later extended to the £5 notes. At the time of their introduction the existing designs on the backs of some of the notes were slightly modified in order to accommodate the markings.

STERLING CURRENCY SYSTEM AND ABBREVIATIONS

One Pound (£1) = Twenty Shillings (20s.)
One Shilling (1s.) = Twelve Pence (12d.)
One Guinea (£1 1s.) = One Pound One Shilling or Twenty-one Shillings
One Pound sterling = Twelve Pounds Scots

From 15 February 1971 the Pound sterling has been subdivided into 100 new pence, abbreviated p to distinguish from (old) pence.

Illustrations are at half linear sizes of the originals throughout.

Catalogue

The Aberdeen Banking Company
The Banking Company of Aberdeen

1749–1754

Established in 1749 by four Aberdeen merchants, this was the first Scottish bank outside Edinburgh to issue notes. The Edinburgh banks not unnaturally retaliated by exerting pressure on the newcomer. Eventually it was forced into voluntary liquidation in January 1754 but left no debts.

1750

1	**Twenty Shillings**	A	Black : uniface
2	**Ten Pounds**	A	Black : uniface

The title The Banking Company *of* Aberdeen distinguishes it from the later and better known Banking Company *in* Aberdeen, details of which follow.

The Aberdeen Banking Company
The Banking Company in Aberdeen

1767–1849

Founded on joint stock lines with a nominal capital of £72,000 and over 100 shareholders, it opened for business on 1 January 1767. It had the declared intention of arresting the "circulation of a variety of Bank Notes from distant and remote parts of the Kingdom issued and signed by People for the most part unknown in this Part of the Country". Aberdeen was now about to strike back at the Edinburgh banks! This was a singularly prosperous bank with branches in several places in the north-east. It amalgamated with the Union Bank of Scotland in July 1849 but its influence was such that it was permitted to continue business under its own name until 1855. It had an Authorised Circulation of £88,467.

THE BANKING COMPANY IN ABERDEEN (contd.)

1773
1   **Ten Pounds**   w   Black: uniface
Arms of Aberdeen flanked by "Ten Pounds" in ornate style, and
"Sterling" in upper and lower-case letters. Inscribed "hereby
obliged to pay . . .". Printed date 1 May 1773 and numbered by
hand. Signed by the Cashier and two others.

1780
2   **One Pound**   A   Black: uniface
Arms of Aberdeen flanked by "One Pound" and "Sterling" in ornate style. Inscribed "promise to pay to . . ." Dated and numbered
by hand. Signed by the Cashier and the Teller. Engraved on a
copper plate by M. Ashby, London.

1781
3   **One Pound**   A   Black: uniface
Similar to the previous £1 note but with printed date 2 May 1781.
Embossed with the Bank's seal.

1786
4   **One Pound**   A   Black: uniface
As previous £1 note but with minor differences in detail. Printed
dates recorded are 2 May 1786 and 2 December 1799, the latter
note having an embossed revenue stamp.
5   **Twenty Pounds**   w   Black: uniface
General design similar to that of the £10 note of 1773. Printed
date 1 May 1786.

Unissued notes of Nos. 4 and 5 and inscribed "Specimen" by hand
are held by the Bank of Scotland.

1797
6   **One Guinea**   A   Black: uniface
Arms of Aberdeen at top left with "One Guinea" at the right.
Printed date 1 May 1797 but numbered by hand. Signed by the
Cashier and the Teller. Designed by – McNaughtan and engraved
on copper plate by Kirkwood & Son.
7   **Five Pounds**   w   Black: uniface
Arms of Aberdeen flanked on the left by "£5" and on the right by
"Aberdeen". Printed date 6 July 1797. Signed by the Cashier and
the Teller. Embossed revenue stamp. Designed by Tomkins and
engraved by M. Ashby.

9

8   **Twenty Pounds**   w   Black: uniface
     Details as in the £5 note but with the Arms flanked by "20" and
     "Aberdeen". Printed date 6 July 1797. Signed by the Cashier and
     the Teller. Embossed revenue stamp.

1799
9   **Five Shillings**   A   Black: uniface
     Shield of the City Arms supported by two thistles at top left with
     "Five Shillings" at the right. Printed date 2 September 1799.
     Numbered by hand and made payable to A. Morrice. Designed by
     G. Paton and engraved on copper plate by Kirkwood & Son.

1801
10   **Twenty Pounds**   w   Red: uniface
     Details as previous £20 note (No. 8) but now printed in red.
     Printed date 1 August 1801.

1810
11   **One Pound**   A   Black: uniface
     General design similar to the earlier £1 note but with "Aberdeen"
     in smaller letters. Dated and numbered by hand. Printed revenue
     stamp on the back.

     Nos. 1–11 have a distinctive and ornate watermark consisting of
     "The Banking Co. in Aberdeen" in three lines.

On amalgamation with the Union Bank of Scotland in 1849 the Aberdeen
bank continued to operate under its own name until about 1855. New
types of notes were issued during this period, produced from steel plates

THE BANKING COMPANY IN ABERDEEN (contd.)

11

engraved by W. H. Lizars. The general design is common to all denominations but with varying vignettes. The main feature is a portrait of Queen Victoria supported by figures representing Medicine and Commerce with the Arms of Aberdeen appearing at the bottom of each note. Underneath the bank's title and in small letters are the words "Established in 1767 and incorporated with the Union Bank of Scotland in 1849". The various constituent banks forming the Union Bank are named in the border surrounding the design. The notes are dated and numbered by hand and signed by the Cashier and the Teller.

1849

12   **One Pound**   A   Black: uniface
    Vignettes of Britannia with shield bearing the Lion Rampant of Scotland and of Plenty with cornucopia are at left and right of the note.
    (*a*) Numbered by hand.
    (*b*) Printed number (1854).

13   **Five Pounds**   W   Black: uniface
    Vignettes of figures representing Commerce and Industry at left and right.

14   **Twenty Pounds**   W   Black: uniface
    Two equestrian statues replace the figures at left and right.

Printers' proofs of these three values exist.

Aberdeen Commercial Banking Company 1778–1833

Founded by Aberdeen merchants in 1778 but little has been recorded of
the history of this bank. It undoubtedly flourished, however, as by 1826
each £500 share was worth £12,000! In 1833 it amalgamated with the
National Bank of Scotland.

1817

1   **One Pound**   A   Black: uniface
   Oval vignette of harbour scene flanked by "One Pound" and
   "Aberdeen". Dated and numbered by hand. Signed by the Cashier
   and one other.

   A contemporary forgery of excellent quality is known.

I

1830

2   **One Pound**   A   Black: uniface
   Engraving of early steam vessel entering Aberdeen Harbour.
   Dated and numbered by hand. Engraved on steel by W. & A. K.
   Johnston. Two signatures.
   Proofs exist.

ABERDEEN, MONTROSE, DUNDEE, EDINBURGH & GLASGOW EXCHANGE & DEPOSIT BANKS
See John Maberly & Company.

THE ABERDEEN TOWN & COUNTY BANKING COMPANY
See The Town & County Bank Limited.

THE AIR (AYR) BANK
See Douglas Heron & Company.

Arbroath Banking Company   1825–1844

Established at Arbroath in May 1825 with a capital of £100,000. When it amalgamated with the Commercial Bank of Scotland on 15 July 1844 it had a note circulation amounting to £13,787 and deposits of £133,279.

1825

1   **One Pound**   A   Black: uniface
Vignette of Arbroath Abbey flanked by "One" and "Pound". Designed by T. Forrester and printed from a copper plate engraved by Kirkwood & Son. Printed revenue stamp on back. Dated and numbered by hand. Signatures of Cashier and Accountant.

1840

2   **One Pound**   A   Black: uniface
Vignette of Arbroath Abbey. The panel on the left illustrates the lighthouse on the Bell Rock. Engraved on steel by W. H. Lizars. Printed revenue stamp on back. Dated and numbered by hand. Signatures of Cashier and Accountant.

Proofs of the basic plate of the 1840 issue are known printed in several colours. These are experimental and all issued notes were printed in black.

3   **Five Pounds**   w   Black: uniface
Similar.

4   **Twenty Pounds**   w   Black: uniface
Similar.

These £5 and £20 notes are known to have been issued but have not been seen. It is doubtful if any have survived.

AYR BANKING COMPANY
See Hunters & Company

The Ayrshire Banking Company   1830–1848

Established at Ayr in April 1830 with a subscribed capital of £200,000. It amalgamated with the Western Bank of Scotland in 1845 at which time there were nine branches in the south-west of Scotland. The Authorised Circulation was £53,656.

1830
  1 **One Pound**   A   Black: uniface
      The design includes an attractive engraving of a sailing vessel entering Ayr Harbour. Dated and numbered by hand. Engraved on steel by W. H. Lizars. Signatures of Manager and Accountant. Proofs known.
      A proof by W. H. Lizars of a note of similar design but with an ornamental framework in blue has been seen but it is not thought that this type was issued.

BANK OF MONA, Branch of The City of Glasgow Bank, q.v.

Bank of Scotland   1695–

As well as being Scotland's oldest bank, the Bank of Scotland has the distinction of being the only bank to have been constituted by the old Scottish Parliament, the native Act "For the Erection of a Publick Bank" being passed on 17 July 1695. The Bank of England had been founded in the previous year by a Scotsman so it is perhaps fitting to record that one of the principal promoters of the Bank of Scotland was an Englishman, John Holland, who became the first Governor.

Unlike the Bank of England this is not a "State" bank but a joint stock commercial bank operating in the same manner as the other Scottish banks. In its early days, however, it did perform one State function, that of calling-in and disposing of the old Scots coinage after the Union of the Parliaments in 1707. The Act constituting the Bank also gave it a monopoly of banking in Scotland for a period of 21 years, but strangely enough no steps were taken for a renewal of that monopoly when it expired. A result of this was the formation in 1727 of the Royal Bank of Scotland and a period of intense rivalry between the "Old Bank" and the "New Bank"

BANK OF SCOTLAND (contd.)

commenced. This rivalry was intensified by the fact that rightly or wrongly the "Old Bank" was accused of Jacobite leanings while the "New Bank" was a staunch Hanoverian supporter. By the middle of the eighteenth century the rivals had learned to live with each other and with the British Linen Company which had by then entered the field. There is no doubt but that the strength of Scottish banking owed much to the solidity and dependability of the three old "Chartered" banks.

The career of the Bank of Scotland was one of steady progress. In 1868 it absorbed the Perth-based Central Bank of Scotland and in 1907 the Caledonian Bank of Inverness. Of greater importance, however, was the absorption of the Union Bank of Scotland Ltd. in 1955 and the British Linen Bank in 1969. As a consequence of these amalgamations the Bank now has deep roots in every part of Scotland and these are effectively maintained by its large branch system.

The Authorised Circulation under the 1845 Act was £300,485; the circulation at March 1975 was £93,800,000.

The first Scottish banknotes were issued by the Bank of Scotland in 1695. Measuring 255 x 116 mm they differ considerably in size and format from traditional Scottish issues. They have no vignette or emblem, are signed by the Accountant and the Treasurer, and are embossed with the Bank's seal.

1695

1	**Five Pounds**	255 x 116 mm		Black: uniface
2	**Ten Pounds**			
	Similar			
3	**Twenty Pounds**			
	Similar.			
4	**Fifty Pounds**			
	Similar.			
5	**One Hundred Pounds**			
	Similar.			

Although it has been suggested in some quarters that notes for 20s. were issued in 1699 this cannot be confirmed. The first £1 note to be recorded was issued on 7 April 1704 and is referred to in the minutes of the Bank as a "twenty shilling" note. No specimen appears to have survived and the earliest seen is dated 1716. From that date there were frequent changes in the design but all are inscribed £12 Scots. They are devoid of any emblem or vignette, relying for security on the fineness of the engraving and on a vertical panel at the left of the note consisting of interwoven letters. The legend reads "The Governour & Company of yᵉ Bank of Scotland, constituted by Act of Parliament, do hereby oblige themselves to pay to . . . or the Bearer Twelve Pounds Scots on Demand". They are headed with the number, "Edinburgh" and a printed date and are signed by the Accountant and the Treasurer "by order of yᵉ Court of Directors." All are embossed with the seal of the Bank and are printed on watermarked paper.

1704

6 **Twenty Shillings** 118 × 126 mm   (presumed to be in the same format as later issues)

7 **Twelve Pounds Scots** 118 × 126 mm Black: uniface

1716

8 Twelve Pounds Scots 118 × 126 mm Black: uniface
Headed "Edenburgh". Legend in lower-case Roman type. "By Order" in fancy script. Printed date 16 April 1716.
There was a contemporary forgery of this note, the first Scottish forgery to be recorded.

1723

9 **Twelve Pounds Scots**   Black: uniface
Similar format to previous issue. Headed "Edinburgh" and drawn in a mixture of types. "Directors" in larger Gothic letters. Vertical panel on the left has solid upper and lower parts. Printed date 24 June 1723.

9

BANK OF SCOTLAND (contd.)

1731
10   **Twelve Pounds Scots**   Black: uniface
        Format as before. Headed "Edin.ʳ" and with "Governour" and
        "Parliament" contracted to "Govern.ʳ" and "Parliam.ᵗ" Printed
        date 4 February 1731.

On 19 November 1730 the Bank began to issue £5 notes bearing the
Option Clause.

1730
11   **Five Pounds**   255 × 116 mm   Black: uniface
        With Option Clause ". . . or in the Option of the Directors Five
        pounds two shillings and six pence sterling at the end of Six
        Months after the Day of the demand." Signed by the Accountant
        and the Treasurer.

On 12 December 1732 £1 (£12 Scots) notes bearing the Option Clause were
issued in a design which appears to have remained in use until after 1748,
three notes in the collection of the Bank of Scotland being dated 12
December 1732, 25 March 1741 and 2 June 1748, the dates inserted by
hand. Signed by the Accountant and the Teller.

1732
12   **One Pound**   A   Black: uniface
        With Option Clause ". . . or in the Option of the Directors One
        Pound Sixpence Sterling at the end of Six Months after the day of
        the demand".

In 1750 the entire range of denominations was issued bearing the Option
Clause, the £1 note appearing in several forms and with differing curved
decorations in the panel on the left.

1750
13   **One Pound**   A   Black: uniface
        Option Clause as before. Inscribed "By Order of the Directors"
        instead of by the "Court of Directors".

14   **One Pound**   A   Black: uniface
        As previous note but with narrower curves in the decoration at the
        left.

15   **One Pound**   A   Black: uniface
        Legend all in italic type with the exception of "Directors", which is
        in Gothic script.

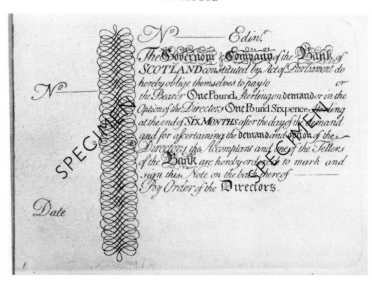

13

16   **Five Pounds**   255 × 116 mm   Black: uniface
Vertical panel at left of interwoven letters. The only specimen of
this note held by the Bank is dated 1 September 1751 and is signed
by the Accountant and the Treasurer, each endorsing "Sixty
Pounds Scots" above his signature. Option Clause similar to
previous £5 note.

17   **Ten Pounds**   Black: uniface
Similar format to £5 note. "Ten Pounds" in large Roman upper
and lower-case type. Option Clause reads ". . . or Ten Pounds five
shillings sterling at the end of Six Months after the Day of the
Demand".

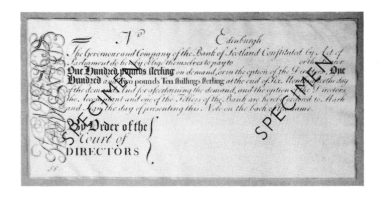

BANK OF SCOTLAND (contd.)

18   **Twenty Pounds**   Black: uniface
     Similar format to the £5 note. "Twenty" in Gothic script. Option
     Clause reads "or in the Option of the Directors, Twenty pounds
     ten shillings . . . etc."

19   **Fifty Pounds**   Black: uniface
     Similar format to the £5 note. "Fifty Pounds" in large Roman
     capitals. "Fifty one Pounds five shillings" of the Option Clause
     and "By order of the" are in Gothic script.

20   **One Hundred Pounds**   Black: uniface
     Similar format to the £5 note. "One Hundred Pounds Sterling",
     "One Hundred" in the Option Clause, and "By Order of the" are
     all in Gothic script. The Option Clause reads ". . . or in the option
     of the Directors, One Hundred and Two pounds Ten Shillings
     sterling . . . etc."

About 1760, £10 and £20 notes were issued without the Option Clause.
These are inscribed "for value received" and the only issued note seen, a
£20 note dated 15 August 1764, has "this to be repaid in the Company's
notes" added by hand to "for value received". The notes are signed by the
Accountant and the Treasurer, and the significance attached to the special
wording is not known.

1760

21   **Ten Pounds**   W   Black: uniface
     Inscribed "for value received".

22   **Twenty Pounds**   W   Black: uniface
     Similar

An entirely new series of high-denomination notes appeared about this
time. The exact date of issue is uncertain as only plate proofs have been
seen, but 1760 may be taken as the approximate date. These notes are
drawn in an italic type of script with variations in particular sections of the
legend. They are of the same size and format as the previous high-value
notes and may be recognised by the figure of the value at the top left of the
design, which is placed within a small solid oval surrounded by a series of
flourishes. There is also a vertical panel of flourishes at the left which varies
in each denomination.

1760

23   **Five Pounds**   Black: uniface
     "Court" in Gothic script. Option Clause as No. 11.

24 **Ten Pounds**   Black: uniface
    "Governour", "Company", "Bank", "Scotland" and "Twenty"
    are all in Roman capitals. "Directors" in Gothic script. Option
    Clause as No. 17.

25 **Twenty Pounds**   Black: uniface
    "Governour" and other words in Roman type similar to the £10
    note. Option Clause as No. 18.

26 **Fifty Pounds**   Black: uniface
    Similar prominent words to those in the £20 note are now in
    Gothic script. Option Clause as No. 19.

27 **One Hundred Pounds**   Black: uniface
    "Bank . . . Scotland", "One Hundred" and "By Order . . . Direc-
    tors" all in Gothic script surrounded by a series of flourishes. Op-
    tion Clause as No. 20.

In the same year a 10s. note was prepared for the first time. Proofs of this
note exist but no issued specimen has been seen. It does not bear an
Option Clause.

1760
28 **Ten Shillings**   A   Black: uniface
    "Ten Shillings" in italic capitals at the top of the note. Ad-
    ditionally inscribed £6 Scots. Printed date 15 May 1760.

The Option Clause was prohibited under the provisions of the Act of 1765
and a new series of notes omitting the Clause was issued. The new notes
may be distinguished from any of the foregoing by the spelling of "Gover-
nor". They are signed by the Accountant and the Teller. The panel of
flourishes at the left of the design varies with each denomination as also
does the type setting of "By Order of the Court of Directors".

1765
29 **One Pound**   A   Black: uniface
    "Governor & Company" in Gothic script within a series of
    flourishes. Printed date 1 August 1765.
    Plates 1, 2, 3 and 4 were used.

30 **Five Pounds**   Black: uniface
    Format as previous £5 note. Value in oval panel at top left similar
    to the 1760 series.

31 **Ten Pounds**   Black: uniface
    Similar in general design to the £5 note but with variations in the
    type used for certain portions of the legend.

32 **Twenty Pounds**
    Similar.

BANK OF SCOTLAND (contd.)

33 **Fifty Pounds**
      Similar.

34 **One Hundred Pounds**
      Similar.

On 2 May 1768 a note for 1 guinea was issued for the first time by this bank.

1768

35 **One Guinea**   A   Black: uniface
      "One Guinea" in a solid panel at the top of the note. Signed by the Accountant and the Teller. Printed date 2 May 1768.
      Plates 1, 2, 3 and 4 used.

The second 1 guinea note was issued on 2 February 1774 and is noteworthy in that it was the first banknote issued by the Bank of Scotland printed in two colours. The basic plate containing the major part of the design was printed in black and a secondary plate, engraved with a panel bearing "One Guinea" similar to that of the 1768 note and a vertical panel of interwoven letters at the left, was superimposed in blue on the basic printing. The complete design is very similar to that of the 1768 note.

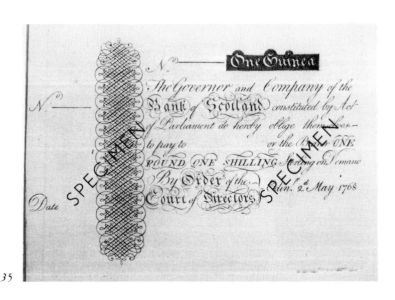

35

1774

36 **One Guinea** A Black and blue: uniface.
Printed date 2 February 1774. Signed by the Accountant and the Teller.
Two basic and two secondary plates were prepared.

A new series was prepared in 1780 which was to remain current until the end of the century. The quality of the copper plate engraving is noticeably improved. All notes are signed by the Accountant and the Teller.

1780

37 **One Pound** A Black: uniface
"One Pound" at top centre in a series of flourishes. Plate reference letter G, H or K at top right. Letters "ND" at top left.

38 **One Guinea** A Black: uniface
"One Guinea" in a series of flourishes at top centre flanked at the left by the number (inserted by hand) and on the right by the printed date, the earliest seen being 1 March 1780 (Plate B). Plates B, C, D, E, F, G are recorded, and Plates H to S with the letters "ND" at top left.

39 **Five Pounds** W Black: uniface
"Edinburgh" in large Gothic letters within a series of flourishes appears at the top, flanked by "£5" and printed year date.

38

BANK OF SCOTLAND (*contd.*)

39

40 **Ten Pounds**   w   Black: uniface
   "Edinburgh" in italic type at top centre flanked by the number
   and "£10" at left and the handwritten date at right. The year 1780
   is printed.

41 **Twenty Pounds**   w   Black: uniface
   Similar to the £10 note.

The first emblem or vignette to appear on a note of the Bank of Scotland
was that of Scotia bearing a thistle in a small oval surmounted by a crown.
This was on a series issued in 1810, which included notes of the unusual
denominations £2 and 2 guineas. Three firms were involved in engraving
the plates for this series, W. & D. Lizars, W. H. Lizars and John Menzies.

1810

42 **One Pound**   A   Black: uniface
   Female figure in oval surmounted by a crown and flanked by
   "One" and "Pound" against a pictorial background. The vertical
   panel at the left consists of the Bank's Arms flanked by "Bank of"
   and "Scotland". Dated and numbered by hand but with a printed
   serial or plate number prefixing the handwritten number. Signed
   on behalf of the Accountant and the Teller. Payable to George
   Sandy.
   (*a*) Engraved by W. & D. Lizars. Plate M. Period after Scotland in
       the vertical panel.
   (*b*) Engraved by W. H. Lizars. Plate M. No period after Scotland.

42(b)

43 **One Guinea**   A   Black: uniface
Similar vignette to that of the £1 note but flanked by "One" and
"Guinea" in curved letters against a pictorial background. Vertical
panel at the left also similar to that on the £1 note. Dated and
numbered by hand and signed on behalf of the Accountant and
the Teller. Payable to George Sandy.
(*a*) Engraved by W. & D. Lizars. Plate G.
(*b*) Engraved by John Menzies. Plate D.

43(b)

BANK OF SCOTLAND (contd.)

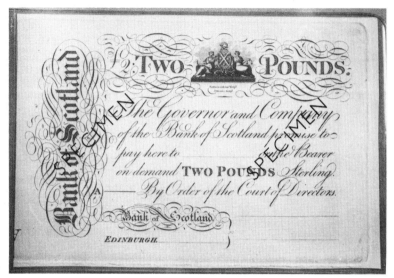

44

44   **Two Pounds**   w   Black: uniface
       Arms of the Bank at top centre flanked by "Two" and "Pounds"
       within a series of flourishes. "Bank of Scotland" placed vertically
       at the left, also within a series of flourishes. Dated and numbered
       by hand and signed on behalf of the Accountant and the Teller.
       Designed by – Butterworth Jr. and engraved by John Menzies.
       Plate A.

45   **Two Guineas**   w   Black: uniface
       Arms of the Bank surmounted by "Two Guineas" in curved letters
       and flanked by "£2.2–" and date and "Bank of Scotland, Edin-
       burgh". Vertical panel similar to that of the £2 note. Dated and
       numbered by hand and signed on behalf of the Accountant and
       the Teller. Designed by – Butterworth Jr. and engraved by John
       Menzies. Plate A.
       Contemporary forgeries of both the £1 and 1 guinea notes are
       known.

At the same time a new series of large-denominational notes was issued.
These are similar in general design to the previous "large" notes and also
without any emblem or vignette, but are made payable to George Sandy.
The vertical panel at the left consists of "Bank of Scotland" within a series
of flourishes but differing in form for each denomination.

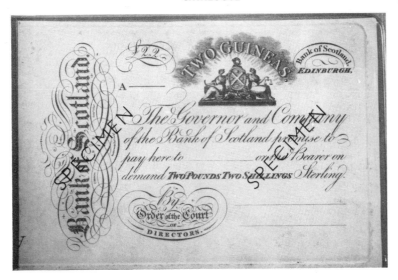

45

1810

46   **Five Pounds**   w   Black: uniface

"Edinburgh" in Gothic letters within a series of flourishes at top centre flanked on each side by "£5". Numbered and dated by hand. Designed by G. Butterworth, Dumfries, and engraved by H. Ashby, London.

47   **Ten Pounds**   w   Black: uniface

"Edinburgh" in italic script flanked by "£10" and the handwritten date. Numbered by hand. There is no engravers' imprint on this note.

48   **Twenty Pounds**   w   Black: uniface

Similar in general design to that of the £10 note. Dated and numbered by hand. No engravers' imprint.

The next series of notes appeared about 1825. It was printed from steel plates engraved by W. H. Lizars and the very ornate designs contrast strangely with the comparative lack of embellishment of the earlier issues. Forgeries of the low-value notes of the 1810 issue no doubt influenced the decision to embrace the greater security offered by steel engraving. The series is particularly interesting in view of its very early adoption of engine turning (the geometric lathe) to give this security.

1825

49   **One Guinea**   A   Black: uniface

Arms of the Bank flanked on each side by "One Guinea". Two vertical panels at left and right each containing a classical female

BANK OF SCOTLAND (contd.)

50

figure. Across the centre of the design is a further panel of concentric geometric patterns. Dated and numbered by hand. Payable to George Sandy. Plate A.

50 **Five Pounds**   w   Black: uniface
Arms of the Bank flanked on each side by "Five Pounds". Two vertical panels as on the 1 guinea note but containing different figures. A panel of similar type to that of the 1 guinea note extends across the centre. Dated and numbered by hand. Payable to George Sandy.

Proofs of the above two notes exist.

51 **Five Pounds**   w   Black: uniface
Arms of the Bank flanked on each side by "Five Pounds" "Bank of Scotland" inscribed within the top side of a thick ornamental border which surrounds the design. Two classical figures appear at each side of a large oblong panel which forms the centre of the note and which contains the legend. Dated and numbered by hand and signed on behalf of the Accountant and the Treasurer.

This note has been seen in Proof form only and may be an unadopted design.

Plates for the £1, £10, £20 and £100 notes were engraved on steel by Perkins Bacon & Petch (later Perkins Bacon & Co.). The design consisted of the Bank's Arms at top centre, flanked on each side by oval panels containing the value. A broad vertical panel at the left consists of a thistle pattern embracing three geometric panels, the centre one of which contains the crowned figure of Scotia. This basic design remained in use for many years.

1825

52   **One Pound**   A   Black: uniface
        Dated and numbered by hand. Payable to George Sandy and signed on behalf of the Accountant and the Teller.
        (*a*) Imprint reads "Perkins Bacon & Petch".
        (*b*) Imprint reads "Perkins & Bacon" (1833).
        (*c*) Imprint reads "Perkins Bacon & Co." Payable to Archd. Bennet.

53   **Ten Pounds**   W   Black: uniface
        Details as £1 note.

54   **Twenty Pounds**   W
        Similar.

55   **One Hundred Pounds** W
        Similar.

W. H. Lizars produced a new design for the £5 note *circa* 1850. This consists of a representation of the Bank's Arms at top centre against a background of the Head Office, the Royal Scottish Academy and the Scott Monument, the entire vignette being flanked by "Five, Edinburgh" on the left and "Five, date" on the right. Four allegorical figures, two on each side of the note complete the design. Payable to Archibald Bennet and signed on behalf of the Accountant and the Treasurer. This note, which is beautifully

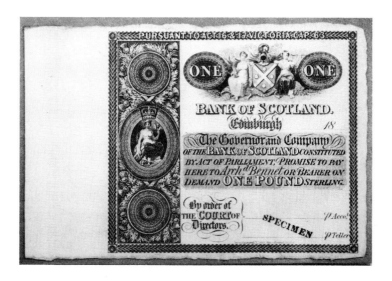

52(*c*)

BANK OF SCOTLAND (contd.)

engraved, has been seen in proof form only and it is not certain if an actual
issue took place as about this time the £5 denomination was added to the
series produced by Perkins Bacon & Co.

1850
  56 **Five Pounds**   w   Black: uniface
       Engraved on steel by W. H. Lizars. *Seen in proof form only.*
       (*a*) Without inscription above the vignette.
       (*b*) Inscribed "Pursuant to Act 16 & 17 Victoria Cap. 63" above the
       vignette.

The custom of making notes payable to a named official or to bearer was
dispensed with about this time and the Perkins Bacon plates were
modified; the entire series was now issued "payable to bearer" only.

1851
  57 **One Pound**   A   Black: uniface
       As previous issue but payable to bearer and not to a named
       official.
  58 **Five Pounds**   w   Black: uniface
       New denomination added to the Perkins Bacon range and of
       similar general design.
  59 **Ten Pounds**   w
       As previous issue but payable to bearer
  60 **Twenty Pounds**   w
       Similar.
  61 **One Hundred pounds**   w
       Similar.

In the summer of 1856 several photographic forgeries of the £1 note
appeared and to meet this new danger the Bank considered printing the
existing notes in blue. Three proofs of the £1 note in blue were prepared
by Perkins Bacon & Co. but apparently no further steps were taken at this
time.

1856
  62 **One Pound**   A   Blue: uniface
       Exists in proof form only.

In 1857 the Bank, being not entirely satisfied with the work of Perkins
Bacon & Co., decided to approach Messrs. Bradbury & Evans with a view to
replacing the existing plates. Instructions were given for the production in

the first instance of a plate for the £100 denomination and this was completed in 1858. Proofs of this design are known but it is not thought that any notes from it were issued and the Bank resumed relations with Perkins Bacon & Co.

1858

63 **One Hundred Pounds**   w   Black: uniface
      Arms of the Bank at top centre flanked by "Bank of" and "Scotland". A vertical panel containing the Arms is at the left. *Seen in proof form only.* Engraved by Bradbury & Evans.

64 **One Hundred Pounds**   w
      As above but with large figures "100" printed in red across the face of the note. *Seen in proof form only.*

The danger of forgery by photographic process influenced the Bank to print in two colours and an opportunity was taken to prepare new plates for the entire series. The design, by Alexander Christie, Master of the Edinburgh School of Design, follows the general principles of the previous series but the vertical panel on the left is replaced by one showing the obverse and reverse of the Great Seal of Scotland as it was at the time of the Bank's establishment in 1695. A lithographic panel containing the words of value in large letters was added to the basic design, in red for all denominations except the £100 note, which was in green. The first notes were delivered in January 1860. Printed date and number and signed on behalf of the Accountant and by the Teller. Engraved and printed by Perkins Bacon & Co.

1860

65 **One Pound**   A   Black and red: uniface
66 **Five Pounds**   w
      Similar.
67 **Ten Pounds**   w
      Similar.
68 **Twenty Pounds**   w
      Similar.
69 **One Hundred Pounds**   w   Black and green: uniface

Proofs of the £1 note in blue and red were prepared but notes were not issued in these colours.

In 1880 the Bank embarked on a period of extensive research into methods of preventing forgery, particularly by photo-mechanical processes. Colours formed an important aspect of this research and for experimental purposes the Bradbury & Evans plate for the £100 note was utilised to produce the basic design for experimental notes in a multiplicity

BANK OF SCOTLAND (contd.)

65

of colours. There were four basic designs for these experimental notes but to these were added various overlays. Altogether these experimental notes present a very colourful series but of course none were put into circulation. Their existence, however, is worth recording.

66

1880

70   **One Hundred Pounds**   W

Experimental notes from the Bradbury & Evans plate with additional facings in several colours. Four basic designs utilised. *In proof form only.*

The experiments were finalised by the adoption of a colour scheme of brown, yellow and blue-grey produced from inks devised by Professor Crum Brown, Professor of Chemistry at Edinburgh University, colours which were to remain standard for all Bank of Scotland notes for the next eighty years. Entirely new designs were prepared by William S. Black, an Edinburgh art teacher, and consisted of the Bank Arms flanked on each side by the value. The vertical panel on the left contains three vignettes, the uppermost showing the equestrian figure of William of Orange from the obverse side of the Great Seal of Scotland as in 1695, the reverse of which is shown on the lower vignette. Between the two is a representation of the Scottish Arms with the date 1695. The notes bear the printed signature of the Secretary, J. F. Stormonth Darling and were produced by means of a lithographic process by George Waterston & Sons, Edinburgh. The watermark consisted of a complex Celtic design which was eventually patented by the Bank. It was generally believed that these notes could not be forged by any photographic process.

1885

71   **One Pound**   A   Brown, yellow and blue-grey:
                                             uniface

72   **Five Pounds**   W
     Similar.

71

BANK OF SCOTLAND (contd.)

72

73   **Ten Pounds**   w
        Similar.

74   **Twenty Pounds**   w
        Similar.

75   **One Hundred Pounds**   w
        Similar.

        Proofs of all values are known.

Two years after the introduction of the above "forgery-proof" new series high-quality forgeries of the £1 note made their appearance. These were the work of a 74-year-old engraver named Mitchell and were produced from a copper plate and not by any photographic means. Only 34 forgeries were produced but the Bank decided that further protection should be added to the design of the notes consisting of a large medallion in blue-grey in the centre of the note and an additional ornamental overlay to cover the blank "white" section of the design.

    In addition to the printers' imprint (which was altered in 1917 from "G. Waterston & Sons Edin." to "G. Waterston & Sons Ld.") there is an additional imprint reading "RD.No.18970". This refers to the patenting of the watermark design.

1889

76 **One Pound**   A   Brown, yellow and blue-grey
                                         uniface
   (*a*) Imprint "G. Waterston & Sons Edin."
   (*b*) Imprint "G. Waterston & Sons Ld."

77 **Five Pounds**   w   Brown, yellow and blue-grey
   Panels of value in black.   uniface
   (*a*) First imprint.
   (*b*) Second imprint.

78 **Ten Pounds**   w   Brown, yellow and blue-grey
   Panels of value in black.   uniface
   (*a*) First imprint.
   (*b*) Second imprint.

79 **Twenty Pounds**   w   Brown, yellow and blue-grey
   Panels of value in red.   uniface
   (*a*) First imprint.
   (*b*) Second imprint.

80 **One Hundred Pounds**   w   Brown, yellow and blue-grey
   Panels of value in red.   uniface
   (*a*) First imprint.
   (*b*) Second imprint.

All notes have the printed signature of the Secretary.

Secretaries: J. F. Stormonth Darling; D. McNeill; S. Macdonald; A. Rose.

76

BANK OF SCOTLAND (contd.)

Recorded printings of the £1 note

21 Aug 1889	13 Jul 1907	22 Sep 1911	15 Jan 1912
14 May 1913	19 Jan 1914	29 Apr 1914	1 Jun 1914
15 Jul 1914	18 Jan 1915	1 Feb 1915	26 Aug 1915
15 Feb 1916	19 May 1916	3 Jun 1916	3 Feb 1917
25 Jun 1917	9 Aug 1917	16 Oct 1917	5 Dec 1917
17 May 1918	12 Jul 1918	9 Oct 1918	7 Nov 1918
1 Dec 1918	12 Dec 1918	20 Feb 1919	30 Mar 1919
17 Apr 1919	8 May 1919	20 Jun 1919	2 Oct 1920
8 Dec 1920	3 Aug 1922	27 Sep 1922	7 Jun 1923
14 Jun 1923	3 Aug 1923	21 Aug 1923	26 Oct 1923
15 May 1924	4 Jul 1924	18 Jul 1924	14 Aug 1924
10 Nov 1924	23 Dec 1924	12 Mar 1925	4 Apr 1925
27 Apr 1925	7 May 1925	24 Jul 1925	6 Aug 1925
16 Sep 1925	30 Aug 1926	13 Sep 1926	10 Oct 1927
16 Nov 1927			

In 1929 the £1 note was reduced in size, retaining in its design most of the features of its predecessor. The left panel, however, now consists of the Royal Arms of Scotland and omits the two illustrations of the Great Seal. The back is printed for the first time and has an illustration of the Head Office. All other denominations retain their former size but the printed signatures of the Governor and the Treasurer replace that of the Secretary.

The "G. Waterston & Sons Ld." imprint is now in use, but the "RD. No." is absent.

1929

81   **One Pound**   B   Brown, yellow and blue-grey
     Reduced size. Back printed with illustration of the Head Office.
     Signatures of the Governor and the Treasurer.

81

82

82   **Five Pounds**   w
     As previous issue but with signatures of the Governor and the
     Treasurer.

83   **Ten Pounds**   w
     Similar.

84   **Twenty Pounds**   w
     Similar.

85   **One Hundred Pounds**   w
     Similar.

Governor: Lord Elphinstone.
Treasurers: G. J. Scott; A. W. M. Beveridge.

Recorded printings of the £1 note

28 Feb 1929	26 Sep 1929	14 Nov 1929	11 Mar 1930
19 Jun 1930	6 Aug 1931	15 Apr 1932	10 Oct 1932
17 Jul 1933			

In 1935 as a result of representations made by the Lord Lyon King of
Arms, the Scottish Royal Arms were replaced on the side panel by those of
the Bank on the £1 note and by a thistle between two unicorns in the larger
denominations. A further modification to the £1 note was the re-designing

BANK OF SCOTLAND (*contd.*)

86

of the central medallion which has now a solid grey background. The back of this note was also modified to include a surrounding oblong frame to the illustration of the Head Office. The registered number of the water-mark appearing as an imprint on notes of £5 and upwards was omitted from 1960. Printed signatures of the Governor and the Treasurer. Printed by George Waterston & Sons Ltd. from plates prepared by Hislop & Day Ltd., Edinburgh.

1935

86 **One Pound**   B   Brown, yellow and blue-grey
Bank Arms instead of Royal Arms. Re-designed medallion. Framed illustration on back.

87 **Five Pounds**   W
As previous £5 note but Royal Arms replaced by a thistle motif.

88 **Ten Pounds**   W
Similar.
(*a*) With watermark registered number imprint.
(*b*) Without imprint (1960).

89 **Twenty Pounds**   W
Similar.
(*a*) With imprint.
(*b*) Without imprint.

90 **One Hundred Pounds**   W
Similar.
(*a*) With imprint.
(*b*) Without imprint.

Governors: Lord Elphinstone; Lord Bilsland.
Treasurers: A. W. M. Beveridge; J. Macfarlane; J. B. Crawford.

90(b)

Recorded printings of the £1 note

15 Jan 1935	4 Feb 1935	18 May 1935	15 Jun 1935
9 Dec 1935	30 Nov 1936	8 Mar 1937	15 Sep 1937
5 Jan 1939	12 Jan 1939	20 Apr 1939	12 Jun 1939
24 Aug 1939	15 Feb 1940	4 Jul 1940	7 Jan 1941
1 Mar 1941	2 Jun 1942	16 Oct 1943	

A further modification to the £1 note took place in 1945, the left panel being dispensed with altogether. In fact the entire design on the front of the new note corresponds in size and detail with the legend panel of the £5 note. A prominent representation of the Bank's Arms appears on the back, flanked on each side by "L1". Printed signatures of the Governor and the Treasurer. From 28 January 1947 the back was printed in a lighter shade.

1945

91   **One Pound**   B   Brown, yellow, blue-grey and grey

  (*a*) Back printed in brown.
  (*b*) Back printed in a lighter shade of brown.

Governor: Lord Elphinstone.
Treasurer: J. B. Crawford.

Recorded printings of the £1 note

4 Jan 1945	6 Feb 1945	29 Mar 1945	4 Jun 1945
4 Oct 1945	27 Nov 1945	28 Jan 1947	9 Sep 1947
4 Oct 1947	5 Jan 1948	10 Feb 1949	8 Mar 1949
4 Oct 1950	5 Jan 1951	12 Oct 1951	5 Nov 1951
17 Sep 1952	22 Oct 1952	4 Sep 1953	9 Oct 1953
16 Oct 1953	22 Oct 1953	9 Nov 1953	

BANK OF SCOTLAND (contd.)

91

In 1950 the £5 note was reduced in size, the design and details being unchanged except that the background of the panels of value is brown instead
of black. For the first time the £5 note now has a printed back, the design
representing the shield element of the Bank's Arms flanked on each side by
"£5".

1950

92   **Five Pounds**   x
     As previous £5 note but in reduced size. Panels of value in brown.
     Printed back.

On 1 March 1955 the £5 note of the previous issue appeared with the
background of the central medallion in blue instead of grey and the
background of the panels of value in black instead of brown.

1955

93   **Five Pounds**   x
     As previous issue but with medallion in blue and panels of value in
     black.

The absorption of the Union Bank of Scotland Ltd. was the occasion of
further modifications in the design of the £1 and £5 notes. The medallion
on the £1 note appears in blue and the back of both notes has been entirely
re-designed to incorporate the Ship motif of the Union Bank.

1955

94   **One Pound**   B   Brown, yellow and light blue
     Back printed with the Ship motif of the Union Bank. Other details
     as before.

95 **Five Pounds** x Brown, yellow and light blue
Panels of value in black. Re-designed back.

Governors: Lord Elphinstone; Sir John Craig; Lord Bilsland.
Treasurer: Sir William Watson.

Recorded printings of the £1 note

1 Mar 1955	2 Mar 1955	3 Mar 1955	4 Mar 1955
1 Sep 1955	2 Sep 1955	6 Sep 1955	12 Apr 1956
10 Sep 1956	11 Sep 1956	13 Sep 1956	14 Sep 1956
30 Aug 1957	1 Oct 1957	2 Oct 1957	3 Oct 1957
4 Oct 1957	7 Oct 1957	16 Aug 1958	18 Aug 1958
25 Aug 1958	26 Aug 1958	27 Aug 1958	28 Aug 1958
29 Aug 1958	3 Oct 1958	7 Oct 1958	1 Dec 1959
30 Nov 1960			

There was a further reduction in the size of both the £1 and £5 notes in 1961, the designs remaining basically unchanged apart from some modifications in the design on the backs.

1961

96 **One Pound** c Brown, yellow and blue
Reduced size.

97 **Five Pounds** z Brown, yellow, blue and black
Reduced size.

Governors: Lord Bilsland; Lord Polwarth.
Treasurers: Sir William Watson; James Letham.

96

BANK OF SCOTLAND (contd.)

97

Recorded printings of the £1 note

10 May 1961	10 Nov 1961	16 Nov 1961	21 Nov 1961
22 Nov 1961	3 Dec 1962	4 Dec 1962	6 Dec 1962
7 Dec 1962	10 Dec 1962	11 Dec 1962	3 Feb 1964
4 Feb 1964	5 Feb 1964	6 Feb 1964	7 Feb 1964
10 Feb 1964	11 Feb 1964	12 Feb 1964	13 Feb 1964
4 May 1965	5 May 1965	6 May 1965	7 May 1965
10 May 1965			

The old "William S. Black" yellow note, first seen in 1885, appeared in its
final form in 1966 when the previous £1 note was modified to accommodate "Edinburgh" and the date at the right of the note instead of below
the signatures, which are now of the Governor and the Treasurer &
General Manager. Notes of £5 and above also bear the altered designation
of the Treasurer. Magnetic sorting marks were added to the £1 note in
1967.

1966

98   **One Pound**   C   Brown, yellow and blue
      (*a*) Without sorting marks on back.
      (*b*) With sorting marks.

99   **Five Pounds**   Z
      As previous issue but signature of Treasurer now designated
      "Treasurer & General Manager".

100   **Twenty Pounds**   W
      Similar.

101   **One Hundred Pounds**   W
      Similar.

Governor: Lord Polwarth.
Treasurer & General Manager: James Letham.

Recorded printings of the £1 note
    1 Jun 1966   1 Oct 1966   3 Mar 1967

A limited number of "Specimen" notes of all denominations and issues of
the William S. Black design dating from 1885 were prepared for restricted
distribution within banking circles.

A number of proofs, essays and experimental notes are known.

An interesting experimental note with edge CMC 7 encoding in connection with the development of the Crossfield note-sorting machine was
produced in 1963 but it is not thought that any were put into circulation.

The William S. Black designs, in spite of many modifications, having
been in use for over eighty years, it was decided in 1968 to replace them
with more modern designs. The new notes, limited at first to £1 and £5
denominations, were printed by George Waterston & Sons Ltd. from plates
prepared in Holland by Joh. Enschede of Haarlem. Metallic strips were incorporated arranged to read B O S in morse code and magnetic sorting
marks appear on the back. The design consists of the Bank Arms in a
central position within a geometric pattern. Panels containing the value are
at top right and bottom left of the design. The back consists of three panels
containing the appropriate Arms. In 1969 "Edinburgh" and the date
appeared in larger letters on the £1 note. Printed signatures of the Governor and the Treasurer & General Manager.

1968

102	**One Pound**	D	Green, blue and multicolour. Back printed in brown and multicolour.

    (*a*) Edinburgh and Date in small letters.
    (*b*) Edinburgh and Date in larger letters.

103	**Five Pounds**	z	Blue and multicolour

102

BANK OF SCOTLAND (contd.)

108

Recorded printings of the £1 note

17 Jul 1968   18 Aug 1969

Designs for £20 and £100 notes were prepared for this series but as the contract for printing passed to Thomas De La Rue & Co. Ltd. their issue was not proceeded with.

As a result of the merger in 1970 with the British Linen Bank a new series of designs was prepared to incorporate features of the notes of both banks. Plates were prepared by Thomas De La Rue & Co. Ltd. in designs which were on similar general lines for all denominations, consisting of a portrait of Sir Walter Scott at the right with a thistle motif in a balancing position at the left. In the centre the Bank's Arms are featured. The back has the shield

108 reverse

emblem at top centre flanked by the Ship emblem of the old Union Bank and the figure of Pallas, emblem of the British Linen Bank. Printed signatures of the Governor and the Treasurer & General Manager.

1970

104	**One Pound**	D	Green and multicolour
	Portrait of Sir Walter Scott.		
105	**Five Pounds**	z	Blue and multicolour
106	**Twenty Pounds**	x	Purple and multicolour
107	**One Hundred Pounds**	x	Red and multicolour

Governors: Lord Polwarth; Lord Clydesmuir.
Treasurer & General Manager: T. H. Walker; A. M. Russell.

Recorded printings of the £1 note

10 Aug 1970   31 Aug 1971   7 Nov 1972   30 Aug 1973
28 Oct 1974

1974

108	**Ten Pounds**	Y	Brown and multicolour

THE BANKING COMPANY IN ABERDEEN
See the Aberdeen Banking Company (2)

THE BANKING COMPANY OF ABERDEEN
See the Aberdeen Banking Company (1)

Bannockburn Iron Works

Because of the scarcity of specie, a number of firms engaged in metallurgy began to issue notes. Most of these were located in England and Wales but at least two companies in Scotland are known to have become part-time bankers.

1774

  1 **One Pound** (£12 Scots)   A   Black: uniface
        Vignette consisting of Lion Rampant within a wreath. Dated and numbered by hand. Two signatures.

I

BATSON BERRY & COMPANY
See the Tweed Bank

BATSON BERRY & LANGHORN
See the Tweed Bank

John Belsh & Company   1804–1806

Established at Stirling in 1804. This was a very small concern and had a
career of only two years. It failed in 1806.

1804
  1 **Five Shillings**   A   Black: uniface
      Printed date (28 December). It bears the inscription "We promise
      to give the bearer on demand at our Office here, one Twenty Shill-
      ing bank note for four of this description".
      Central vignette of Stirling flanked by "Five" and "Shillings".
      Signed "John Belsh & Co." with one additional signature.

The British Linen Bank   1746–1969
The British Linen Company

To anyone not well versed in Scottish history, "The British Linen Company" may seem a strange choice of title for a bank, but of course banking
was not envisaged as one of its activities at the outset. As its name implies it
was created for the purpose of encouraging the linen trade and the banking
side did not develop until later although promissory notes were issued very
early in its history. Not in fact until 19 March 1849 was the Company for-
mally recognised as a banking corporation but for the greater part of the
preceding century banking had become its prime function.

The Company was incorporated by Royal Charter of George II dated 5
July 1746 with an authorised capital of £100,000 and it was agreed "that a
seal be made for the Company in the figure of Pallas" – an emblem which
was to appear on most of its notes. The early notes were inscribed "for
value received in goods", indicative of the commercial activities of the
Company. As the banking side grew the inscription became "for value
received" and finally was omitted altogether. Gradually the commercial
operations ceased and the Company withdrew from manufacturing and
trading activities in 1763, devoting itself entirely to the more profitable
business of banking. With the passing of the years it grew in stature and by
the end of the century had taken its place alongside the senior Chartered

THE BRITISH LINEN BANK (contd.)

Banks, the Bank of Scotland and the Royal Bank, as the mainstay of the Scottish banking system.

In the nineteenth century in common with the other banks it developed an extensive branch system but in its long history only absorbed one other bank, the Paisley Banking Company. In 1906 the title of the Company was changed to the more appropriate one of "The British Linen Bank". Barclays Bank Ltd. acquired the whole of the capital in 1919 but in 1969 sold the holding to the Bank of Scotland and a merger between the two Scottish banks became effective from 1970.

The British Linen Company had an Authorised Circulation under the 1845 Act of £438,024 and the actual circulation at the time of the merger with the Bank of Scotland was around £18 million.

The first promissory notes were issued before banking became one of the activities of the company. The early notes were therefore inscribed "for value received in goods".

1747

  1 **Five Pounds**   w   Black: uniface
      Inscribed "for value received in goods. Payable without interest."

  2 **Ten Pounds**   w
      Similar.

  3 **Twenty Pounds**   w
      Similar.

  4 **One Hundred Pounds**   w
      Similar, but bearing interest after three months.

Notes for 10s. and £1 were issued in 1750.

1750

  5 **Ten Shillings**   A   Black: uniface
      Inscribed "for value received in goods".

  6 **One Pound**   A
      Similar.

1754

  7 **Twenty Shillings**   A   Black: uniface
      Circular vignette at top left of seated female figure with ship under sail in background; vertical panel of flourishes at the left of the design. Dated and numbered by hand. Inscribed "for value received in goods". Signed on behalf of the Manager and by the Accountant.

9

1763

8 **Five Pounds** w Black: uniface

Vignette consisting of the Bank emblem in an ornate frame at top left. Vertical panel of flourishes at the left. With Option Clause "... or in the option of the Directors Five Pounds two shillings and sixpence sterling at the end of six months after the day of the Demand". Inscribed "for value received in goods". Dated and numbered by hand and signed by the Manager and the Accountant, each endorsing the words "Five Pounds" above his signature.

1768

9 **One Guinea** A Black: uniface

Bank's emblem at top centre flanked on the left by the date and on the right by "One Guinea". A panel consisting of thistles extends across the top of the note. Inscribed "value received" – the words "in goods" now being omitted. Printed date 5 April 1768 but numbered by hand. Signed on behalf of the Manager and by the Accountant.

1770

10 **One Guinea** A Black: uniface

Bank's emblem at top centre flanked by "Edinr 6 Septr 1770" (printed) and "One Guinea". Panel of thistles at top similar to previous issue. Numbered by hand and signed on behalf of the Manager and by the Accountant.

1780

11 **Five Pounds** w Black: uniface

Emblem of Pallas at top left in circular frame. "Edinburgh" in Gothic type within a series of flourishes top centre. Vertical panel

THE BRITISH LINEN BANK (contd.)

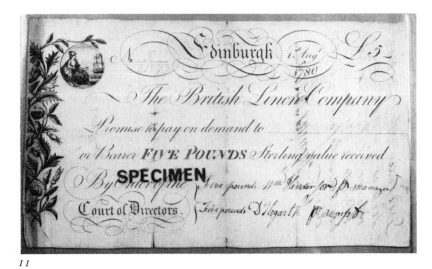

11

of thistles and roses at left. Printed date 1 August 1780. Signed on behalf of the Manager and the Accountant, each officer prefacing his signature with the words "Five Pounds".

1797

12   **Five Shillings**   127 × 90 mm   Black: uniface
Bank emblem at top left. Panel of flourishes extending across the top of the note. Printed date 31 March 1797. Numbered by hand. Payable to David Sime and signed on behalf of the Manager and by the Accountant.

12

1808

13   **One Guinea**   A   Black: uniface
Panel with a thistle and rose motif extending across the top of the
note and containing the year "1808" in the centre. Bank emblem
at top left. Date "October 180–" printed at the end of the legend.
Numbered by hand. Payable to William Fleming and signed on
behalf of the Manager and by the Accountant.

The inscription "for value received" is omitted from all following issues,
except where indicated.

1811

14   **Twenty Shillings**   A   Black: uniface
"Twenty Shillings" in Gothic script and within a series of
flourishes at top. Bank emblem at the left. Dated and numbered by
hand. Payable to William Fleming and signed on behalf of the
Manager and by the Accountant.
Contemporary forgery dated 30 May 1811.

1815

15   **One Guinea**   A   Black: uniface
Similar in general design to that of the 1 guinea note of 1808 but
the oval panel at the top contains "B L C" instead of "1808".
Dated and numbered by hand. Payable to William Fleming and
signed on behalf of the Manager and by the Accountant.
Contemporary forgery dated 1 September 1815.

15

THE BRITISH LINEN BANK (contd.)

16

1821

16   **Twenty Shillings**   A   Black: uniface
Bank emblem at top centre flanked by "Twenty" and "Shillings" in Gothic script. Dated and numbered by hand. Payable to David Dow and signed on behalf of the Manager and by the Accountant.
Contemporary forgery dated 18 May 1825.

17   **One Guinea**   A   Black: uniface
Two seated female figures at top centre surmounted by "One Guinea" in curved letters. Vertical panel of thistles at the left. Dated and numbered by hand. Payable to David Dow and signed on behalf of the Manager and the Accountant. Designed by John Beugo and engraved by T. Forrester.

18   **Five Pounds**   w   Black: uniface
Small vignette of the Bank emblem at top left with a vertical panel of roses and thistles forming the left of the design. "British Linen Company" and the value in large Gothic script. Inscribed "value received". Dated and numbered by hand and signed by the Manager and the Accountant.

19   **Twenty Pounds**   w
Similar.

20   **One Hundred Pounds**   w
Similar.

In 1822 an entirely new series was issued in a design which apart from some modifications was to remain standard throughout the remainder of the nineteenth century. The notes were printed from steel plates engraved by

Perkins Fairman & Heath (later Perkins Bacon & Co.). The design, common to all denominations, consists of the Royal Arms flanked by panels containing the value. The vertical panel at the left has the Bank emblem in the centre with oval panels of engine-work above and below (a very early use). Dated and numbered by hand and signed on behalf of the Manager and the Accountant.

1822

21	**One Pound**	A	Black: uniface
22	**One Guinea** Similar.	A	
23	**Five Pounds** Similar.	W	
24	**Ten Pounds** Similar.	W	
25	**Twenty Pounds** Similar	W	
26	**One Hundred Pounds** Similar.	W	

Contemporary lithographic forgeries of the £1 note are known dated 2 November 1826, 1 May 1828 and 1 March 1829.

To give protection against the possibility of forgery by means of photography, the above series was issued in 1861 printed in blue with "B.L.Co." in large letters superimposed in red as an additional security measure. Other details are unchanged. The first issue was dated 1 September 1860 but was not issued to the public until the following year.

22

THE BRITISH LINEN BANK (contd.)

1861

27	**One Pound** Details as previous issue.	A	Blue and red: uniface
28	**Five Pounds** Similar.	W	
29	**Ten Pounds** Similar.	W	
30	**Twenty Pounds** Similar.	W	
31	**One Hundred Pounds** Similar.	W	

Defects in the blue ink became apparent. This was inclined to oxidize and become almost black. New notes were issued printed with an improved ink and in the same design apart from the introduction of small background panels to incorporate the date and number, these being now printed.

1871

32	**One Pound** Printed date and number.	A	Blue and red: uniface
33	**Five Pounds** Similar.	W	
34	**Ten Pounds** Similar.	W	

32

35

35 **Twenty Pounds** w
   Similar.
36 **One Hundred Pounds** w
   Similar.

In 1904 because of an internal dispute which had taken place among the directors of Perkins Bacon & Co. Ltd. and which resulted in a Receiver being appointed, the bank deemed it advisable to transfer the contract for printing notes to Waterlow & Sons Ltd. New plates embodying most of the

36

THE BRITISH LINEN BANK (contd.)

37

features of the previous issue were prepared. The main difference in design lay in the vertical panel at the left which was considerably altered. The signature on behalf of the Manager is printed but notes were still signed by hand on behalf of the Accountant. The first notes were dated 28 February 1905 but were not issued to the public until 18 April of that year.

1905

37	**One Pound**	A	Blue and red: uniface
38	**Five Pounds**	W	

Similar, but both signatures hand-signed.

39	**Ten Pounds**	W

Similar.

40	**Twenty Pounds**	W

Similar.

41	**One Hundred Pounds**	W

Similar.

Proofs of all denominations of the 1871 and 1905 issues are known.

The title of the Bank was changed in 1906 from the British Linen Company to the more appropriate one of the British Linen Bank, and the existing plates were altered accordingly. Notes of £5 and upwards continued to have both signatures hand-signed and in 1912 the printed signature of the £1 note was changed to that of the General Manager as a result of the altered designation of that official. The first notes were dated 15 January 1907 and were issued to the public on 5 March of that year.

1907

42   **One Pound**   A   Blue and red: uniface
        (*a*) Printed signature of Manager.
        (*b*) Printed signature of General Manager (1912).

43   **Five Pounds**   W   Blue and red: uniface
        As previous issue but inscribed "British Linen Bank".

44   **Ten Pounds**   W
        Similar.

45   **Twenty Pounds**   W
        Similar.

46   **One Hundred Pounds**   W
        Similar.

In 1914 at the suggestion of Waterlow & Sons a lithographic "sunburst" overlay in red was superimposed on the £1 note and on the remaining values in the following year. Additional security was afforded in the form of a printed back, the design by M. Meredith Williams being in blue and featuring the Bank emblematic figure of Pallas in a panel of engine-work.

42

THE BRITISH LINEN BANK (contd.)

47

1914
47 **One Pound**   A   Blue and red: back printed in blue

1915
48 **Five Pounds**   W
    Similar.
49 **Ten Pounds**   W
    Similar.

49

50 **Twenty Pounds** w
    Similar.

51 **One Hundred Pounds** w
    Similar.

Recorded printings of the £1 note

9 Feb 1916	3 Aug 1916	18 Jul 1917	5 Apr 1918
19 Mar 1923	31 Jul 1924	15 Oct 1925	

The £1 note was reduced in size in 1926, the design retaining the general features of the previous issue but now having one signature (printed) only, that of the Cashier.

1926

52 **One Pound** B   Blue and red: back printed in blue

    Reduced size.

Recorded printings

1 May 1926	1 Mar 1927	4 Oct 1927	31 Oct 1928
2 Dec 1929	30 Nov 1931	8 Feb 1932	26 Jan 1933
3 Apr 1933	10 Aug 1933		

In 1935, following objections from the Lord Lyon King of Arms to the inclusion of the Royal Arms on the notes, new Arms specially prepared for the Bank were substituted. The design was otherwise unaltered. The £1 note at first had the printed signature of the Cashier, but from 1945 this was replaced by that of the General Manager. Notes of £5 and upwards had the printed signature of the General Manager and were additionally hand-signed on behalf of the Accountant. From 1942 both signatures were printed on the £5 note, the designation of the Accountant being changed to that of Accountant and Cashier. From 1945 all notes bear the printed signature of the General Manager alone.

52

THE BRITISH LINEN BANK (*contd.*)

53

1935

53   **One Pound**   B   Blue and red: back printed in
                                         blue

    Arms of Bank instead of Royal Arms.
    (*a*) Printed signature of Cashier.
    (*b*) Printed signature of General Manager (1945).

54   **Five Pounds**   W   Blue and red: back printed in
                                         blue

    (*a*) One printed and one manuscript signature.
    (*b*) Two printed signatures (1942).

54(b)

55 **Ten Pounds** W
   Similar
   (*a*) Two signatures.
   (*b*) One signature (1945).

56 **Twenty Pounds** W
   Similar
   (*a*) Two signatures.
   (*b*) One signature (1945).

57 **One Hundred Pounds** W
   Similar
   (*a*) Two signatures.
   (*b*) One signature.

General Managers: G. Mackenzie; A. P. Anderson; T. W. Walker.

Printings of the £1 note

18 Jan 1935	20 Feb 1935	15 Mar 1935	22 Apr 1935
9 Feb 1937	2 Jul 1937	4 Oct 1937	8 Nov 1938
3 Oct 1939	7 Mar 1940	16 May 1940	18 Jul 1940
3 Oct 1940	20 May 1941	23 Jun 1941	25 Jul 1941
27 Aug 1941	14 Jul 1942	20 Aug 1942	30 Sep 1942
4 Nov 1942	10 Dec 1942	12 Jan 1943	11 Feb 1943
13 Mar 1943	16 Apr 1943	17 May 1943	18 Jun 1943
19 Jul 1943	3 Sep 1943	7 Oct 1943	9 Nov 1943
1 Dec 1943	3 Jan 1944	4 Feb 1944	6 Mar 1944
7 Apr 1944	4 Jan 1946	5 Feb 1946	8 Mar 1946
9 Apr 1946	6 May 1946	3 Feb 1947	4 Mar 1947
6 May 1947	7 Jun 1947	14 Aug 1947	16 Sep 1947
17 Oct 1947	18 Nov 1947	10 Jun 1948	14 Sep 1948
15 Dec 1948	20 Jan 1949	15 Jul 1949	16 Aug 1949
17 Sep 1949	18 Oct 1949	5 Aug 1950	4 Jun 1951
12 Feb 1952	21 Oct 1953	16 Feb 1954	12 Jan 1955
9 Aug 1955	19 Aug 1955	28 Dec 1955	4 Jun 1956
5 Apr 1957	28 Aug 1958	12 May 1959	15 Apr 1960

In 1944 the £5 note was issued in reduced size, the design being unaltered. Other details were also unchanged.

1944
58 **Five Pounds** X Blue and red
   Reduced size.

Thomas De La Rue & Co. Ltd. took over the security printing side of Waterlow & Sons in 1961 and in consequence notes now bear the De La Rue imprint. Other details remain unchanged.

THE BRITISH LINEN BANK (contd.)

60

1961

59   **One Pound**   B   Blue and red
       Thomas De La Rue & Co. Ltd.
       There was only one printing of this note, dated 30 September
       1961.

60   **Five Pounds**   Y   Blue and red
       There was only one printing in this reduced size, dated 2 January
       1961.

61   **Twenty Pounds**   W   Blue and red

62   **One Hundred Pounds**   W
       Similar.

Further reduction in size of the £1 and £5 notes took place in the following year. The design of the £1 note remained basically unchanged but the £5 note was of an entirely new design featuring a portrait of Sir Walter Scott, who had been a customer at the Selkirk branch. Both notes have the printed signature of the General Manager and are engraved by Thomas De La Rue & Co. Ltd.

1962

63   **One Pound**   C   Blue and red
       Reduced size.

64   **Five Pounds**   Y   Blue and red
       Portrait of Sir Walter Scott

       Printings of the £1 note

         31 Mar 1962   1 Jul 1963   4 May 1964   25 Jan 1966
         13 Jun 1967

64

The design on the back of the £1 note was modified in 1967 to accommodate magnetic sorting marks, the Bank emblem now being flanked on each side by the value "One". Part of the printing of 13 June 1967 appeared in this form and as the size and design of the note was changed in the following year this may be regarded as a provisional issue.

1967
  65 **One Pound**   C   Blue and red
        Re-designed back with magnetic sorting marks.

The final British Linen designs appeared on the £1 and £5 notes issued in 1968. The £1 note retains many of the features of its predecessors but now incorporates the portrait of Sir Walter Scott and is further reduced in size. The design of the £5 note presents a somewhat similar appearance to that of the 1962 issue but with alterations in the finer detail of the engraving. The size has also been reduced.

1968
  66 **One Pound**   D   Blue and red
        Portrait of Sir Walter Scott. Reduced size.

65 reverse

THE BRITISH LINEN BANK (*contd.*)

66

Dates of printings: 3 February 1968, 29 February 1968, 5 November 1969 and a final printing (20 July 1970) in which the date is in a heavier type.

67   **Five Pounds**   z   Blue and red
      Reduced size.

"Specimen" notes of all twentieth century issues were prepared in small numbers for limited distribution within banking circles.

The printing of the £1 note dated 31 March 1962 exists with experimental edge encoding in connection with the development of the Crossfield note-sorting machine. These notes were overprinted in red "Cancelled: Test Note" but were not put into circulation.

67

JOHN BRUCE
See The Perth United Company

I

Caithness Banking Company   1812–1825

Established at Wick in October 1812 as a private partnership. It suspended payment in 1825 when the business was taken over by the Commercial Bank of Scotland.

1812

1   **One Pound**   A   Black : uniface
    Oval vignette featuring a schooner in sail with a plough in the foreground. The motto reads "Commoditas et Securitas". Printed date but numbered by hand. Signature of the Manager and additionally countersigned by hand.

2   **One Guinea**   A   Black : uniface
    Similar in general design and details.

Caledonian Banking Company   1838–1907

Founded at Inverness in 1838 with a capital of £125,000, it had a successful career until 1878, when, having taken over from a customer £400 of City of Glasgow Bank stock, it found itself liable as a shareholder when the City Bank failed. Doubt as to the extent of this liability created a panic which resulted in the Bank's suspension. Eventually it was found that the liability would not exceed £11,000 and confidence was restored, the bank resuming business. Its progress, however, proved disappointing and in 1907 an arrangement was made for its absorption by the Bank of Scotland. At the time of the merger, the Caledonian Bank had 34 branches.

CALEDONIAN BANKING COMPANY (contd.)

1838

1 **One Pound**   A   Black: uniface
   Vignette of the town of Inverness and the River Ness with the
   Castle in the background. Two plates, A and B, similar in detail
   were prepared, engraved on steel by W. H. Lizars. Dated and
   numbered by hand and signed by the Manager and the Accountant.

2 **Five Pounds**   w   Black: uniface
   Vignette of Inverness Castle against a background showing the
   town and river. Other details as in the £1 note.

3 **Ten Pounds**   w
   Similar.

4 **Twenty Pounds**   w
   Similar.

5 **One Hundred Pounds**   w
   Similar.

The Gaelic motto on the surrounding border reads "Tir nam Beann, nan
Gleann, s'nan Gaisgeach", the translation being "Land of the Mountains,
the Glens and the Heroes". The notes of the Caledonian Bank are the only
Scottish issues having a Gaelic inscription apart from a motto incorporated
in one of the Leith Banking Company notes.

3

1892 issue from 1838 plate

1863

6 **One Pound**   A   Black: back printed in blue
New vignette of the River Ness and Inverness Castle. The design on the back incorporates the arms of some of the towns in which the Bank had branches. Designed and engraved on steel by W. & A. K. Johnston. Printed date. Plate D 1863, Plate F 1872.

7 **Five Pounds**   w   Black: back printed in blue
Printed by W. & A. K. Johnston from the Lizars plate. Design and details as before, but with printed number.

8 **Ten Pounds**   w   Black: uniface
As previous £10 note but bearing the imprint of W. & A. K. Johnston.

9 **Twenty Pounds**   w
Similar.

10 **One Hundred Pounds**   w
Similar.

1872

11 **Five Pounds**   w   Black and red: uniface
As previous £5 note but with a panel containing "Five" printed in red over the legend panel. The printed back is discontinued on this issue. Printed date and number.

In 1882 the Bank registered under the Companies Act of 1879 and the title was changed to the Caledonian Banking Company Limited. All notes of the previous issues available for re-issue were impressed with the new title vertically across the left of the design by means of a rubber stamp either in black or in blue.

In 1883 new plates were prepared by George Waterston & Sons, Edinburgh, the designs being similar to those of the previous issues. The vignette of the £1 note reverted to that of the 1838 design. Panels containing the value in words were superimposed in blue and a lithographic network in orange added as an overlay covering the whole area of the note. Printed date and number and signed on behalf of the Manager and the Accountant.

1883

12 **One Pound**   A   Black and blue with overlay in orange: uniface
Inscribed "Caledonian Banking Company Limited".

13 **Five Pounds**   w
Similar.

14 **Ten Pounds**   w
Similar.

CALEDONIAN BANKING COMPANY (*contd.*)

15 **Twenty Pounds**   w
     Similar.
16 **One Hundred Pounds**   w
     Similar.

Circa 1890 the panels of value were changed from blue to orange, other details remaining unaltered. Printed by George Waterston & Sons, Edinburgh

1890
  17 **One Pound**   A   Black and orange: uniface
  18 **Five Pounds**   w
       Similar.
  19 **Ten Pounds**   w
       Similar.
  20 **Twenty Pounds**   w
       Similar.
  21 **One Hundred Pounds** w
       Similar.

Proofs of all values of the 1838 and 1863 issues are known.

17

18

Campbell Thomson & Company   1787– ?

Founded at Stirling on 6 January 1787. Believed to have issued notes but details of these and of the history of the Company are not known.

CARRICK, BROWN & COMPANY
See the Ship Bank.

The Carron Company

This famous iron company was the second establishment of its kind to issue notes in Scotland during the Napoleonic Wars to meet the need for specie.

1797
1   Five Shillings   A   Black: uniface
     Oval vignette containing arms of the Company (three carronades).
     Printed date May 1797. Numbered by hand. Printed from a
     copper plate engraved by Kirkwood & Son.

THE CARRON COMPANY (contd.)

I

The Central Bank of Scotland   1834–1868

This joint stock bank was established at Perth in 1834 with a capital of
£78,125, later £218,800. After an uneventful career it was purchased by the
Bank of Scotland in 1868. There were 405 shareholders and the Authorised
Circulation amounted to £42,933.

1834

1 **One Pound**   A   Black: uniface
   Vignette of the City of Perth with the River Tay in the foreground.
   Female figures representing Agriculture and Commerce appear at

I

left and right respectively and an illustration of the Head Office is at the bottom of the note. Designed and engraved on steel by W. H. Lizars. Dated and numbered by hand. Signatures of Manager and Accountant.

2 **Five Pounds**   w   Black: uniface
Figure of Britannia holding a spear and supported by Prosperity with cornucopia against a background of shipping on the River Tay. Dated and numbered by hand and signed by the Manager and the Accountant. Engraved on steel by W. H. Lizars.

3 **Ten Pounds**   w   Black: uniface
Figure of Britannia holding a spear and supported by Prosperity with cornucopia against a background of shipping on the River Tay. Other details as £1 note.

4 **Twenty Pounds**   w
Similar.

1861

5 **One Pound**   A   Black and blue: uniface
Modification of the original Lizars design incorporating a panel with the value "ONE" in blue and with the addition of "Pursuant to Act of Parliament" at the top. Engraved on steel by W. & A. K. Johnston.

Proofs of all values known.

1865

6 **One Pound**   A   Black and blue: uniface
Similar to that of the 1861 issue but with printed date (1 November 1865) and number.

5

THE CENTRAL BANK OF SCOTLAND (contd.)

7

1866

7   **Five Pounds**   w   Blue and red: uniface
General design as in the previous £5 note but with the addition of
"Pursuant to Act of Parliament" at the top and with a panel of the
value in large letters superimposed in red over the legend panel.
Printed date and number. Signed by the Manager and the Accoun-
tant. Engraved on steel by W. & A. K. Johnston.

8   **Ten Pounds**   w   Black and blue: uniface
Similar to previous £10 note but with the addition of "Pursuant to
Act of Parliament" at top of the note. "TEN" in large letters
superimposed in blue on the legend panel. Dated by hand but with
a printed number. Signatures of the Manager and the Accountant.
Engraved on steel by W. H. Lizars.

9   **Twenty Pounds**   w   Blue and red: uniface
As previous £20 note but with addition of "Pursuant to Act of
Parliament" at top. Dated by hand but with printed number.
Signatures of Manager and Accountant. "TWENTY" in large letters
superimposed in red over the legend panel. Engraved on steel by
W. & A. K. Johnston.

Unissued specimens of Nos. 7–9 are held in the collection of
the Bank of Scotland.

The City Banking Company of Glasgow   1836
The Glasgow City Bank

An attempt to launch this joint stock bank was made in 1836, but owing to the current economic situation sufficient support was not forthcoming. There is no evidence that it ever transacted business. Notes were prepared for issue, however, and proofs of these exist and are described below. These are engraved on steel but the actual engraver is not known.

This bank must not be confused with the *City of Glasgow Bank* which was formed in 1839.

1836

1   **One Pound**   A   Proof. Black: uniface
Inscribed THE GLASGOW CITY BANK. Vignette showing Commerce seated with Neptune reclining at her side against a background symbolising Industry. Two female allegorical figures are at left and right of the note. Dated and numbered by hand. Signature of Manager and Accountant.

2   **One Pound**   A   Proof. Black: uniface
A second design inscribed THE CITY BANKING COMPANY has an oval vignette showing a panoramic view of Glasgow. Two standing female figures are at left and right of the note. Dated and numbered by hand. Signatures of Manager and Accountant.

3   **Five Pounds**   W   Proof. Black: uniface
Inscribed THE GLASGOW CITY BANK with a vignette of Britannia with trident against a background which includes a sailing ship. Dated and numbered by hand. Signatures of Manager and Accountant.

The City of Glasgow Bank   1839–1879

The strength of the Scottish banking system produced few of the failures which had become a feature in England and elsewhere. In fact there were only three large failures in the whole history of Scottish banking. The most disastrous of all was that of the City of Glasgow Bank. This large joint stock bank was established in January 1839 with 779 shareholders. From the outset it adopted a "progressive and dynamic" outlook – not always the qualities looked for in the conservative business of banking – and its suspension of payment for 33 days during the crisis of 1857 should have been a warning. Having survived this it continued a fraudulent course until

THE CITY OF GLASGOW BANK (contd.)

1 October 1878, when it closed its doors forever with a loss of over £6 million to be borne by its shareholders. Depositors did not suffer and in order to safeguard the high reputation of Scottish banknotes, City notes were duly accepted by the other banks. One result of the failure was the adoption of the principle of limited liability by the remaining banks and large institutions.

The Authorised Circulation under the 1845 Act was £72,921.

All notes were designed and engraved on steel by Gilmour & Dean, Glasgow with the exception of the final type of the £100 note.

1839

1   **One Pound**   A   Black: uniface
Equestrian statue flanked on either side by "One Pound". Dated and numbered by hand. Signatures of the Accountant and Cashier.

1864

2   **One Pound**   A   Black and blue
Vignette of Queen Victoria with oval panels on each side containing the value "One". The back contained a representation of the arms of the City of Glasgow printed in blue. Signatures of the Accountant and Cashier.

3   **Five Pounds**   W   Black and blue
General design as the £1 note but with "Five" in rectangular panels on each side of the Queen's portrait. The bank contains the arms of Glasgow printed in blue. Signatures of the Accountant and Manager, or on their behalf.

4   **Twenty Pounds**   W   Black: uniface
Design similar to that of the £5 note but with figures "20" in circular panels on each side of the Queen's portrait. Other details as in the £5 note.

5   **One Hundred Pounds**   W   Black: uniface
Arms of Glasgow with two female supporters and oval panels on each side containing figures "100". Dated and numbered by hand. Signatures of Accountant and Manager.

Proofs of Nos. 1–5 are known.

1866

6   **One Pound**   A   Black and blue
As preceding £1 note but "Incorporated under Act of Parliament" around the portrait. Printed number and date (12 November). No watermark.

7 **Twenty Pounds**   w   Black and blue
   Design as previous note of this denomination but with large
   figures "20" in blue superimposed on the legend panel. The back
   is now printed in blue with the City Arms. Printed number and
   date (12 November). No watermark.

1877
8 **Five Pounds**   w   Black and blue
   As previous £5 note but with printed number. The signatures are
   now designated "*p*. Accountant" and "*p*. Manager". No watermark.

9 **One Hundred Pounds**   w   Black and blue
   Design as previous £100 note but with large figures "100"
   superimposed on the legend panel. Printed number and date.
   "Pursuant to Act 16 & 17 Victoria Cap.63" added to top of the
   note. "One Hundred Pounds" in top border and "City of
   Glasgow Bank" in the bottom reverses the order in which they
   appear on the earlier note. Printed number and date. The back is
   printed in blue with the City Arms. Printed by Gilmour and Dean
   from a plate prepared by Perkins Bacon & Co., London.

In spite of the failure of this bank, the noteholders were paid in full.

In 1849 the City of Glasgow Bank established a branch in the Isle of Man
under the name BANK OF MONA. It is appropriate, therefore, to add particulars of the separate note issue provided for this branch. Readers are
referred to *Banknotes and Banking in the Isle of Man* by Ernest Quarmby for
full details of its history.

1849
10 **One Pound**   A   Black: uniface
    Central vignette of shipping at entrance to Douglas harbour. Two
    allegorical female figures representing Commerce and Plenty are
    at left and right respectively. Dated and numbered by hand and
    signed by the Manager and one other. Engraved on steel by W. H.
    Lizars.

1850
11 **One Pound**   A   Black: back printed in black
    Vignette of Queen Victoria supported by the lion and the unicorn
    of the Royal Arms. Two female figures at left and right hold
    shields bearing the Arms of Glasgow and of the Isle of Man. The
    design on the back illustrates Castle Rushem. Dated by hand but
    with printed number. Engraved on steel by W. H. Lizars. Signed
    by the Manager and the Accountant.

THE CITY OF GLASGOW BANK (contd.)

1865

12	**One Pound**	A	Black: back printed in blue

Similar in general design to that of the 1850 note but with oval panels containing "One" flanking the portrait of Queen Victoria. The border is redrawn to incorporate "Branch of the City of Glasgow Bank" at top and "Incorporated by Act of Parliament" at bottom. The design on the back is similar to that of the previous note but is printed in blue. Dated by hand but with printed number. Signed by the Manager and the Accountant. Engraved on steel by Gilmour & Dean, Glasgow.

13	**Five Pounds**	w	Black and blue: uniface

Central vignette with shields bearing the Triune of the Isle of Man and the Arms of Glasgow flanked by panels containing figure "5" and printed in blue. Female figures representing Commerce and Britannia with shield bearing the Triune are at left and right respectively. Signed by the Manager and the Accountant. The Basic plate is printed in black and in addition to the panels of value in blue, "Five" in large letters is superimposed on the legend panel in blue.

Clydesdale Bank Limited   1838–
Clydesdale & North of Scotland Bank Limited
The Clydesdale Bank Limited
The Clydesdale Banking Company

As the name suggests, this bank has its roots in Glasgow, having been established there in 1838 with a paid-up capital of £299,400, this figure being increased three years later to £500,000. Its expansion was rapid, due in no small measure to the number of banks which it absorbed in the early years of its history. These were:

> The Greenock Union Bank;
> The Edinburgh & Glasgow Bank (which itself had already absorbed the Edinburgh & Leith Bank, the Southern Bank of Scotland and the Glasgow Joint Stock Bank);
> The Eastern Bank of Scotland (with its own acquisition, the Dundee Commercial Bank).

Its progress was not entirely confined to Scotland as in the 1870s it suddenly opened three branches in Cumberland, including Carlisle, much to the consternation of the English banks which lost no time in referring the matter to Parliament. The Select Committee appointed as a result of this representation failed to make any recommendation when it reported its findings but the Scottish banks took the hint and there were no further incursions into English territory apart from the opening of branches in London.

The capital of the Clydesdale Bank was acquired in 1919 by the Midland Bank. The Midland Bank also purchased the North of Scotland Bank Ltd. in 1923 and from this time a fusion of the Midland's Scottish interests seemed to be a logical step. This did not occur until 1950, however, the Scottish banks merging under the title of the Clydesdale and North of Scotland Bank Limited and thus having a strong representation throughout the entire country. A few years later the cumbersome title was shortened by a reversion to the name "Clydesdale Bank Limited".

The Authorised Circulation under the 1845 Act was £104,028 but this figure increased through its absorption of other banks. The circulation at March 1975 was £39,900,000.

INSCRIBED THE CLYDESDALE BANKING COMPANY

The first notes were issued on the opening day 7 May 1838. They were designed, engraved and printed by W. & A. K. Johnston, Edinburgh, and are of uniform design consisting of the Arms of Glasgow in a circular vignette at top centre, flanked by oval panels containing the value of the note in words. Dated and numbered by hand and signed on behalf of the Manager and the Accountant. A vertical panel of floreate design at the left varies slightly in each denomination.

1838

1	**One Pound**	A	Black: uniface
2	**Five Pounds**	W	Black: uniface
3	**Ten Pounds** Similar.	W	
4	**Twenty Pounds** Similar.	W	
5	**One Hundred Pounds** Similar.	W	

In 1865 a lithographic plate consisting of "Clydesdale Bank" together with a panel containing the value was superimposed in red on the printing from the basic plate. There is a discrepancy in the records here. According to the official history of the Bank a "new design by Hugh Wilson" was issued this year. Certainly the £5 note bears his imprint but it is not a new design. The £20 note bears the imprint of W. & A. K. Johnston, while that for £100 bears no imprint at all.

CLYDESDALE BANK LTD. (contd.)

9

1865

  6 **One Pound**   A   Black and red: uniface

  7 **Five Pounds**   w   Black and red: uniface

  8 **Twenty Pounds**   w
     Similar.

  9 **One Hundred Pounds**   w
     Similar, but lithographic panel reading "Clydesdale Banking Company".

Proofs on card overprinted "Specimen Note" are known.

In 1870 a new type of £1 note was printed from a plate prepared by Thomas De La Rue & Co., London. The design, which presents something of a departure from the traditional Scottish note, is contained within an elaborate framework with "The Clydesdale Banking Company" in large curved lettering at the top and two classical female portraits at left and right joined by a panel containing "One Pound". The colours, green and purple, are also unusual for a Scottish note. Printing appears to have been effected from a lithographic plate and is on much thinner paper than the foregoing issues. The note is signed on behalf of the Manager and by the Accountant.

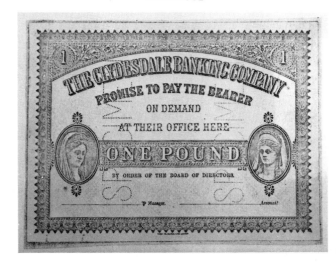

IO

1870

10   **One Pound**   A   Green and purple: uniface
      Printed by Thomas De La Rue & Co., London.

      Unissued notes perforated "Specimen" are known.

In 1878 the £1 note reverted to the design of that of the 1865 issue. This, and all other denominations, were printed on the bank premises, a custom which was to continue for some sixty years. The plates, however, were prepared by professional engravers.

INSCRIBED THE CLYDESDALE BANK LIMITED

A new design for all denominations appeared in 1891 and this is probably the "new design" referred to in the Bank history. It consists of the Arms of Glasgow supported by three female figures representing Commerce, Industry and the Arts placed at top centre and flanked by oval panels containing the value. Two allegorical female figures appear at left and right of the £1 note but are absent from the higher denominations. The basic plate is printed in black while a secondary plate superimposed in red contains the panels of value and "Clydesdale Bank Limited". Both plates were engraved by W. & A. K. Johnston, Edinburgh, and the actual printing carried out at the bank premises. The signature of the Accountant is now printed and there is a manuscript signature on behalf of the General Manager.

CLYDESDALE BANK LTD. (contd.)

11

1891

11	**One Pound**	A	Black and red: uniface
	New design.		
12	**Five Pounds**	W	
	Similar.		
13	**Twenty Pounds**	W	
	Similar.		
14	**One Hundred Pounds**	W	
	Similar.		

A new series was issued in 1922 in the same basic design. The border of the £1 note is re-designed and the whole area of the design is superimposed with a "sunburst" type of overlay in red. Notes of £5 and upwards are unchanged in design. The main feature of this issue, however, is that all values now have printed backs, the design consisting of the Arms of Glasgow within a large panel of engine-work engraving. The basic plates of all denominations are printed in blue as also are the plates for the back design. The secondary plates continue to be printed in red. All notes have the printed signatures of the Cashier and the Accountant and from 1945 those of the General Manager and the Accountant & Cashier. The imprint of the plate engraver appears on notes of £5 and upwards until 1945 and is omitted from that year.

1922

| 15 | **One Pound** | A | Blue and red: back printed in blue |

15

16 **Five Pounds** w Blue and red: back printed in blue

    (*a*) Signatures of the Cashier and the Accountant.

    (*b*) Signatures of the General Manager and the Accountant & Cashier.

17 **Twenty Pounds** w

    Similar.

    (*a*) First two signatures.

    (*b*) Second two signatures.

16(a)

CLYDESDALE BANK LTD. (contd.)

18   **One Hundred Pounds**   w
     Similar.
     (*a*) First two signatures.
     (*b*) Second two signatures.

     The designation "Accountant & Cashier" was changed to "Chief
     Accountant & Cashier" in 1946.

In 1927 the £1 note was reduced in size while retaining all the features of
the previous design. The printed signatures are those of the Accountant
and the Cashier and from 1932 the General Manager and the Accountant &
Cashier. From 1947 the signatures are those of the General Manager and
the Chief Accountant & Cashier. The date in all printings up to 4 April
1945 is in serifed capital letters but after that the date appears in sans serif
type.

1927
19   **One Pound**   B   Blue, red and orange: back printed in blue
     Reduced size.
     (*a*) Signatures of Accountant and the Cashier.
     (*b*) Signatures of the General Manager and the Accountant &
     Cashier (1932).
     (*c*) Signatures of the General Manager and the Chief Accountant &
     Cashier (1947).

Accountant: R. Young.
Cashier: A. Swanson.
General Managers: A. Mitchell; J. J. Campbell.
Accountant & Cashier: R. Young.
Chief Accountant & Cashier: J. W. Pairman; R. R. Houston.

19(b)

Recorded printings

3 Jan 1927	16 Nov 1927	8 Feb 1928	3 Aug 1932
7 Dec 1932	8 Aug 1934	5 Dec 1934	24 Apr 1935
16 Oct 1935	20 May 1936	30 Sep 1936	30 Dec 1936
17 Mar 1937	30 Jun 1937	27 Oct 1937	31 Aug 1938
11 Jan 1939	22 Nov 1939	17 Apr 1940	17 Jul 1940
20 Nov 1940	19 Mar 1941	23 Jul 1941	5 Nov 1941
25 Feb 1942	1 Jul 1942	24 Feb 1943	28 Jul 1943
12 Apr 1944	15 Nov 1944	24 Feb 1945	6 Apr 1945
24 Oct 1945	1 May 1946	20 Nov 1946	19 Mar 1947
3 Sep 1947	7 Apr 1948	26 May 1948	27 Oct 1948
12 Jan 1949	13 Jul 1949	14 Nov 1949	14 Dec 1949

In 1948 the £5 note was issued in the existing design but with a light blue lithographic overlay, other details remaining unchanged. The printed signatures are those of the General Manager and the Chief Accountant & Cashier.

1948

20	**Five Pounds**	W	Blue and red with light blue overlay: back printed in blue

INSCRIBED CLYDESDALE & NORTH OF SCOTLAND BANK LIMITED

In 1950 the North of Scotland Bank Ltd. merged in the Clydesdale Bank under the title of Clydesdale & North of Scotland Bank Ltd., and an en-

20

CLYDESDALE BANK LTD. (contd.)

tirely new series of notes was issued as a result of the merger. The designs are completely different from the previous notes of either of the constituent banks. That of the £1 note has the new Arms of the Bank at top centre with vignettes featuring shipping on the Clyde at the left and an agricultural scene on the right. The serial number is in red. The back contains an engraving of a Highland river scene. Notes of £5 and upwards are in reduced format and illustrate King's College, Aberdeen, on the left and Glasgow Cathedral on the right, the backs having the Bank Arms in a circular panel flanked by the value. All notes bear the printed signature of the General Manager. Steel bands are introduced for the first time and remain a feature in all forthcoming issues.

1950

21	**One Pound**	B	Blue, orange and red: back printed in blue
22	**Five Pounds**	X	Purple and multicolour: back printed in purple
23	**Twenty Pounds**	X	Red and multicolour
24	**One Hundred Pounds**	X	Green and multicolour

General Managers: J. J. Campbell; R. D. Fairbairn.

Recorded printings of the £1 note

| 1 Mar 1950 | 1 Mar 1952 | 1 Mar 1954 | 1 Jun 1955 |
| 1 Nov 1955 | 1 Nov 1956 | 1 May 1958 | |

£1 and £5 notes in new designs and in reduced size appeared in 1961. These were from plates engraved by Thomas De La Rue & Co. Ltd. and show the Bank Arms surrounded by lathe work at the right and a modern

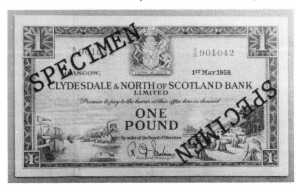

21

22

interpretation of a traditional Celtic design on the left. The back of the £1 note shows a launching scene on the Clyde. The date on this note is in black on the printings of 1961 and 1962 but is in the green colour of the basic plate in that of 1 February 1963. Both notes have the printed signature of the General Manager.

1961

25	**One Pound**	C	Green and multicolour: back
	(*a*) Date in black.		printed in green
	(*b*) Date in green.		
26	**Five Pounds**	Y	Dark blue and multicolour: back printed with a design incorporating the Bank's Arms

Recorded printings of the £1 note

1 Mar 1961   2 May 1962   1 Feb 1963

25(a)

CLYDESDALE BANK LTD. (contd.)

27

INSCRIPTION REVERTS TO CLYDESDALE BANK LIMITED

On the adoption of the shortened title new notes were issued. The £1 and £5 notes are those of the previous issue with the name of the bank altered. Those of the other denominations are of similar general design but have differing engravings on the back. All have the printed signature of the General Manager. On 3 April 1967 the back of the £1 note was slightly modified to accommodate magnetic sorting marks.

1963
27 **One Pound**   C   Green and multicolour
     Inscribed "Clydesdale Bank Limited".
     (a) Without magnetic sorting marks on back.
     (b) With magnetic sorting marks.

28 **Five Pounds**   Y   Dark blue and multicolour

1964
29 **Ten Pounds**   Y   Brown and multicolour
     Back has an illustration of the University of Glasgow.

28

29 reverse

30 reverse

31 reverse

CLYDESDALE BANK LTD. (contd.)

30 **Twenty Pounds**   x   Red and multicolour
     Back has an illustration of George Square, Glasgow.
31 **One Hundred Pounds**   x   Purple and multicolour
     Back illustrates a Highland scene with river and bridge.

A small number of "specimen" notes were prepared for circulation within banking circles.

Recorded printings of the £1 note

  2 Sep 1963   1 Feb 1965   30 Mar 1966   3 Apr 1967
  1 Oct 1968   1 Sep 1969

A new issue commenced in 1971 with designs by Louis Woudhuysen featuring "Famous Scots". Each design has a portrait of a famous Scotsman with the back of the note illustrating a scene associated with that celebrity. The notes all have the printed signature of the General Manager and are on paper bearing a three-masted sailing ship as a watermark. Printed and engraved by Thomas De La Rue & Co. Ltd.

1971
32 **One Pound**   D   Green and multicolour
     Portrait of Robert the Bruce. Back shows him leading the Scottish
     Army at the battle of Bannockburn in 1314
33 **Five Pounds**   z   Blue and multicolour
     Portrait of Robert Burns. Back illustrates a wild rose and a field
     mouse, subjects of two of his most famous poems.
34 **Ten Pounds**   y   Brown and multicolour
     Portrait of David Livingstone. Back illustrates an African scene.

1972
35 **Twenty Pounds**   x   Purple and multicolour
     Portrait of Lord Kelvin. Back illustrates his lecture room at
     Glasgow University.

32

36 **One Hundred Pounds**   x   Red and multicolour
     Portrait and illustration on back similar to those on the £20 note.

A small number of "specimen" notes of all denominations was prepared for circulation within banking circles.

Recorded printings of the £1 note

   1 Mar 1971   1 May 1972   1 Aug 1973

General Managers: R. D. Fairbairn; A. R. Macmillan.

COCHRANE MURDOCH & COMPANY
See the Glasgow Arms Bank

The Commercial Banking Company of Scotland
1810–1959
The Commercial Bank of Scotland
The Commercial Bank of Scotland Limited

The Commercial Banking Company of Scotland opened for business at Edinburgh on 3 December 1810, having been promoted by business men and traders as a large national institution independent of private bankers and with the middle class citizen in mind. The original capital of £3 million is an indication of the size of the project. It justified its national aspiration by embarking on a branch system which in its day became the largest in Scotland. The status of the bank was enhanced in 1831 when it obtained its Royal Charter, but not until 1882 was "Limited" added to its title under the 1879 Companies Act. Two small banks were absorbed by the Commercial, the Caithness Bank in 1825 and the Arbroath Banking Company in 1844. The Authorised Circulation under the 1845 Act was fixed at £374,880 and the actual circulation reached a figure of over £20 million by 1959, the largest circulation in the country at the time. The Commercial was the first British bank to absorb a hire purchase company. In 1959 it amalgamated with the smaller National Bank of Scotland Limited to form National Commercial Bank of Scotland Limited.

The note issue of the Commercial Bank is of great interest to collectors as not only were changes in design numerous but many of these designs were outstanding in their technical and artistic qualities. "Set numbers" were ascribed to the various issues. These were intended purely for accounting purposes and do not always coincide with changes in design. However, the set numbers do provide a built-in reference which is of considerable assistance to collectors. These official set numbers are included in the lists which follow.

THE COMMERCIAL BANKING COMPANY OF SCOTLAND

Except where otherwise indicated, all nineteenth century notes of this bank are signed by or on behalf of the Accountant and the Cashier.

Notes of the first issue were dated 12 November 1810. Only a few of the £1 notes appear to have survived and no details of the design of the other denominations remain on record at the Bank. The Issue was designed by

I

John Beugo and printed from copper plates on the Bank's premises. Each note has an impression of the Bank's seal placed over the signatures and also an embossed revenue stamp. The £1 note has a small oval vignette of Edinburgh Castle flanked by "One Pound Sterling" on the left and "Commercial Bank of Scotland" on the right.

1810

1	**One Pound**	A	Black: uniface
2	**Five Pounds**		
3	**Twenty Pounds**		None of these notes appear to have survived.
4	**One Hundred Pounds**		

Contemporary forgeries of the £1 note exist.

1818

5	**One Guinea**	A	Black: uniface

The only note of this denomination issued by the Commercial Bank. Design somewhat similar to the previous £1 note with a central vignette of Edinburgh Castle. Printed from a copper plate engraved by W. W. Ferguson.

Because of the existence of forgeries new plates were prepared with a more ornate design consisting of a vignette of Edinburgh Castle, larger than that of the previous issue, and the words "One Pound" within a series of ornamental curves. Printed from copper plates engraved by J. Menzies. Until 1823 the notes were payable to Edwd. Robertson (the Secretary) and thereafter to his successor Robert Paul. In 1825 in order to secure ad-

THE COMMERCIAL BANK OF SCOTLAND LTD. (*contd.*)

ditional protection some of the notes were overprinted with an ornamental framework from a steel plate engraved by W. H. Lizars. New £5 notes designed by A. Forrester and engraved by J. Menzies and of similar pattern to the £1 note were issued around this time; £20 and £100 notes were probably issued but no record of them exists.

1818

6 **One Pound**   A   Black: uniface
   (*a*) Payable to Edwd. Robertson.
   (*b*) Payable to Robert Paul (from 1823).
   (*c*) Overprinted with ornamental framework (1825).

7 **Five Pounds**   w   Black: uniface
   Probably not issued until after 1820.

8 **Twenty Pounds**   w ⎱   Presumed to have been issued but
9 **One Hundred Pounds**   w ⎰   no record exists.

Contemporary forgeries of the £1 note exist, most of them being the work of French prisoners of war.

On 1 May 1826 a new £1 note was printed from steel plates engraved by W. H. Lizars. This has a fine engraving of Edinburgh Castle flanked by two medallions. This note was on issue for one year only.

6(*b*)

1826
  10 **One Pound**   A   Black: uniface
        Engraved on steel.

In 1827 new plates for a £1 note were prepared by Perkins & Heath (later Perkins Bacon & Co.) of London. These again have a vignette of Edinburgh Castle flanked by two medallions, that on the left having the head of George IV, and is the first of a series of royal heads appearing on Commercial Bank notes. The medallion on the right bears the allegorical figure of Caledonia while at the bottom there is a similar medallion figure representing Commerce. There is a printed revenue stamp on the back. Payable to Robert Paul.

1827
  11 **One Pound**   A   Black: uniface

THE COMMERCIAL BANK OF SCOTLAND

The Bank was granted its Royal Charter in 1832, the fact being appropriately recorded by modifications to the existing plate. The opportunity was also taken to replace the head of George IV with that of William IV. Until 1835 the notes were payable to Robert Paul and thereafter to J. S. Cunningham. Although numbered by hand the first notes had a printed serial letter and commencing 1832 the first reference to a "set" number appeared, the serial reading 8/A. By 1844 the whole number was printed for the first time.

1832
  12 **One Pound**   A   Black: uniface
        Set 8
        (a) Printed serial: payable to Robert Paul (1832).
        (b) Printed set and serial: payable to J. S. Cunningham (1835).
        (c) Entire serial number printed (1844).

New £5 and £10 notes were printed from steel plates engraved by W. H. Lizars and the technical qualities of these are exceptional. Each has a central vignette of Edinburgh Castle and bears the portrait of William IV. The £10 note has an additional portrait. They have printed revenue stamps on the back and are embossed with the Bank's seal.

1833
  13 **Five Pounds**   W   Black: uniface
  14 **Ten Pounds**   W   Black: uniface
        Proofs of both values are known.

THE COMMERCIAL BANK OF SCOTLAND LTD. (contd.)

13

Steel plates for a new £1 note were prepared by W. H. Lizars. The central vignette consists of Arms with two female supporters and with Edinburgh Castle now relegated to the background. Portraits of Queen Victoria and Prince Albert are on the left and right respectively, and for the first time the new Head Office is shown in an engraving at the bottom of the note. The back has an elaborate steel engraving surrounding the printed revenue stamp. Printed number, dated by hand.

1848

15   **One Pound**   A   Black.

Back also engraved in black.

Proofs of both the front and the back of this note exist.

An entire new series was printed from steel plates engraved by W. H. Lizars. The Castle, for so long a feature of this bank's notes, has disappeared and is now replaced by the allegorical classical figures on the pediment of the new Head Office building. The portraits of Queen Victoria and the Prince Consort are retained and the Head Office again appears at the bottom of the notes. The higher denominations are of the same general design. All have printed numbers but are dated by hand. Printed revenue stamp on the back.

1850

16   **One Pound**   A   Black: uniface

Set 9

17	**Five Pounds**	w	Black : uniface
18	**Ten Pounds**	w	Black : uniface
19	**Twenty Pounds**	w	Black : uniface
20	**One Hundred Pounds**	w	Black : uniface

Proofs of all denominations exist.

Stamp duty being now compounded, notes no longer bore a revenue stamp. A new series of unstamped notes was prepared from steel plates engraved by Perkins Bacon & Co. in the same general design as the previous Lizars issue, but omitting the Royal portraits. All notes were now made payable to the bearer instead of to the secretary.

1856

21	**One Pound**	A	Black : uniface
	Set 10		
22	**Five Pounds**	w	Black : uniface
23	**Ten Pounds**	w	Black : uniface
24	**Twenty Pounds**	w	Black : uniface
25	**One Hundred Pounds**	w	Black : uniface

Proofs of all denominations exist.

Because of the increasing danger of forgery by photographic means, the foregoing series was next printed in blue and a lithographic overlay containing the value superimposed in red on the central portion of the notes. The £1 notes were numbered 11/A to 12/U.

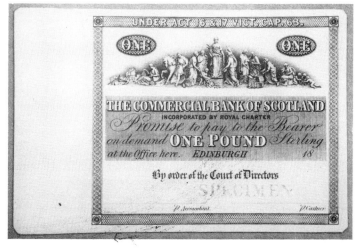

21

THE COMMERCIAL BANK OF SCOTLAND LTD. *(contd.)*

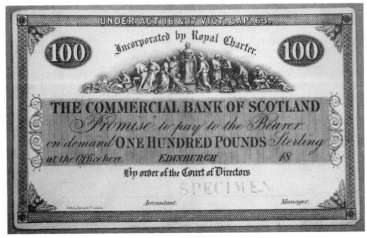

25

1860

26	**One Pound**	A	Blue and red: uniface
	Sets 11 and 12		
27	**Five Pounds**	W	Blue and red: uniface
28	**Ten Pounds**	W	Blue and red: uniface
29	**Twenty Pounds**	W	Blue and red: uniface
30	**One Hundred Pounds**	W	Blue and red: uniface

Proof and "specimen" notes of all denominations exist.

26

THE COMMERCIAL BANK OF SCOTLAND LTD.

The Bank adopted the principle of limited liability in 1882 and the existing plates were modified to include "Limited" in the Bank's title. "Incorporated by Royal Charter and Act of Parliament" now appears on the lower frame. The £1 notes are numbered 12/U101–200 in red to distinguish them from the previous series, and from 13/A onwards in black.

1882

31	**One Pound**	A	Blue and red: uniface

      (a) Set 12 numbered in red (100 notes only).
      (b) Set 13 numbered in black.

32	**Five Pounds**	W	Blue and red: uniface
33	**Ten Pounds**	W	Blue and red: uniface
34	**Twenty Pounds**	W	Blue and red: uniface
35	**One Hundred Pounds**	W	Blue and red: uniface

An entirely new series was issued in 1888 which was to continue with very minor modifications for twenty years. The new plates were by Bradbury Wilkinson & Co. and the notes engraved in blue with a buff lithographic overlay. The back of the notes has an engraving of the Head Office printed in an attractive shade of green. The £1 note comprises sets 14, 15, 16 and 17. From set 15 onwards the Accountant's signature was printed and the printers' imprint modified to read "Bradbury Wilkinson & Co. *Ltd*." Notes of £5 and upwards were hand-signed.

1888

36	**One Pound**	A	Blue and buff, back printed in green

      (a) Set 14 signed by hand. Printers' imprint Bradbury Wilkinson & Co.
      (b) Sets 15, 16 and 17. Printed signature of Accountant. Printers' imprint Bradbury Wilkinson & Co. Ltd.

37	**Five Pounds**	W	Blue and buff, back printed in green
38	**Twenty Pounds**	W	Blue and buff, back printed in green
39	**One Hundred Pounds**	W	Blue and buff, back printed in green

"Specimens" of all denominations are known.

Accountants: James Anderson, 1884–1902; John Gowan, 1902–1903; Lockhart M. Mackay, 1903–1923.

THE COMMERCIAL BANK OF SCOTLAND LTD. (contd.)

36(b)

After the previous series had been in circulation for twenty years, new designs were prepared by Bradbury Wilkinson & Co. Ltd. The main feature of this design was the illustrations of the Bank's principal offices. The Head Office appears at top and the chief offices in Glasgow and London at left and right respectively. All denominations are printed in black from the engraved plates with a lithographic overlay in blue and buff. The backs have a representation of the Bank's arms within a large ornate panel printed in mauve in the £1 notes and in blue in the others. The £1 note bears the printed signature of the Accountant and is additionally hand-signed, while both signatures in the larger denominations are hand-signed. The series was in use for one year only, being modified the following year. Only 500,000 of the £1 notes numbered 18/A to 18/E and considerably fewer of the larger denominations were printed and few indeed appear to have survived.

1908

40	**One Pound**	A	Black with blue and buff overlay. Back printed in mauve. Set 18.
41	**Five Pounds**	W	Black with blue and buff overlay. Back printed in blue. Set 13.
42	**Twenty Pounds**	W	Black with blue and buff overlay. Back printed in blue.
43	**One Hundred Pounds**	W	Black with blue and buff overlay. Back printed in blue.

"Specimens" of all denominations exist.

Accountant: Lockhart Maurice Mackay.

41

Recorded printings: 2 Jan 1908 (all denominations)

The plates of the previous issue were modified to include an oval framework surrounding the illustrations of the Glasgow and London offices and the buff and blue overlay extended to provide a network pattern covering the whole face. The engraved plate was now printed in blue instead of black and otherwise the design was unaltered. All notes now have the printed signature of the Accountant. The colours of the backs are as before. The £1 notes comprise sets 18 (letters F to Z) 19, 20 and 21. Notes of set 19 and some of set 21 are numbered in red, and from 19/L onwards the signature of the Cashier is also printed.

1909

44   **One Pound**   A   Blue with blue and buff overlay.
                                           Back printed in mauve
     (*a*) Set 18: number in black, one printed signature.
     (*b*) Set 19: numbered in red, one printed signature.
     (*c*) Sets 20 and 21: numbered in black, both signatures printed.
     (*d*) Part of set 21: numbered in red, both signatures printed.

45   **Five Pounds**   W   Blue with blue and buff overlay.
                                           Back printed in blue.
     Set 13: printed signature of Accountant. Hand-signed on behalf of the Manager.

46   **Twenty Pounds**   W
     Similar.

47   **One Hundred Pounds**   W
     Similar.

THE COMMERCIAL BANK OF SCOTLAND LTD. (contd.)

44(a)

Accountants: Lockhart Maurice Mackay, 1903–1923; Royden Ritchie Thomson, 1923–1928.

Cashier: Hugh McLaren Roberts, 1920–1928.

Recorded printings of the £1 note

2 Jan 1909	3 Jan 1910	3 Jan 1911	2 Jan 1912
2 Jan 1913	2 Jan 1914	2 Jan 1915	3 Jan 1916
2 Jan 1917	2 Jan 1918	2 Jan 1919	2 Jan 1920
2 Jan 1921	3 Jan 1922	2 Jan 1923	

45

New designs were prepared by Waterlow & Sons Ltd. featuring the portrait of John Pitcairn of Pitcairns, engraved from the Raeburn painting in the possession of the Royal Scottish Academy. Pitcairn was the first Chairman of the Bank in 1810. All denominations are of uniform design and printed in blue with a shaded overlay in yellow and red. These are generally conceded to be one of the finest of Scottish note designs. The £1 notes bear the printed signatures of the Accountant and the Cashier and those of £5 and above of the General Manager and the Cashier, but the first printing of the £5 note was hand-signed on behalf of the Cashier and has the printed signature of the "Manager". The backs show a fine engraving of the Head Office surrounded by a panel of geometric engraving. The £1 notes are numbered 22/Z to 22/W (reversed alphabetical order), 500,000 of each serial being printed, i.e. 2 million in all. The £5 notes comprise sets 14, 15 and 16, the £20 set 13, and the £100 set 11.

1924

48 **One Pound** A Blue with shaded yellow and red
overlay. Back printed in blue
Set 22.

49 **Five Pounds** W
Similar. Sets 14, 15 and 16.
(*a*) Hand-signed on behalf of Cashier and printed signature of Manager.
(*b*) Printed signatures of Cashier and General Manager.

50 **Twenty Pounds** W
Similar. Set 13.

51 **One Hundred Pounds** W
Similar. Set 11.

48

THE COMMERCIAL BANK OF SCOTLAND LTD. (contd.)

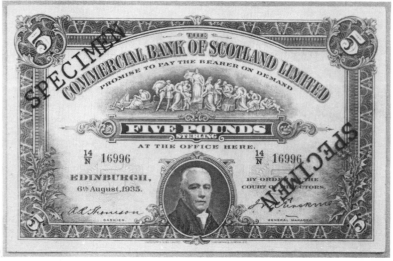

49(b)

Accountant: Royden Ritchie Thomson.

Cashiers: Hugh McLaren Roberts, 1920–1928; Royden Ritchie Thomson, 1928–1940; James Thomson, from 1940.

Recorded printings: £1

    31 Oct 1925   1 Nov 1926

£5, £20, £100: There were numerous printings of these as they continued in issue until 1947.

"Specimens" are known of all denominations.
Printers' proofs of the Pitcairn medallion exist.

To conform with the size of the current Treasury £1 note (and with the forthcoming £1 Bank of England note) the £1 note of the last series was issued in reduced size, the design remaining unchanged. One million notes of each letter from 23A to 23E were printed and 250,000 each from 23F onwards. The serial letters A, B and C were in Gothic capitals while Roman characters were used from D onwards. Set 23 has the set number preceding the serial letter. Sets 24 and part of 25 have the serial letter placed above the set number, and the remainder of set 25 reverts to the set number preceding the serial letter but with the addition at the end of the note number of a triangle in solid colour. Printed signatures of the Accountant

52(c)

– from set 24 designated as Chief Accountant – and the Cashier. Denominations of £5 and upwards of the previous series continued to be issued throughout this period.

1927

52 **One Pound** B Blue with shaded yellow and red overlay

(a) Set 23: serial letters A, B and C in Gothic capitals.

(b) Set 23: serial letters D onwards in Latin capitals, preceded by set number.

(c) Sets 24 and 25: serial letter above set number. Signature of *Chief* Accountant.

(d) Set 25: set number preceding serial letter. Note number followed by triangle.

Accountants and Chief Accountants: Royden Ritchie Thomson, until 1928; Peter Irving, Accountant in set 23, Chief Accountant sets 24 and 25

Cashiers: Hugh McLaren Roberts, 1927; Royden Ritchie Thomson, until 1940; James Thomson, from 1940.

Recorded printings:

1 Dec 1927	1 June 1928	1 Dec 1928	2 Dec 1929
1 June 1931	31 May 1932	31 Mar 1934	1 May 1934
8 Apr 1935	12 Feb 1936	30 Nov 1936	2 Sep 1937
22 Jun 1938	4 May 1939	6 Aug 1940	4 June 1941
6 Jan 1943	4 Jun 1944	2 Dec 1944	

"Specimens" exist.

After 23 years the "Pitcairn" notes were replaced by a new series from plates engraved by Bradbury Wilkinson & Co. Ltd. The new series caused considerable public comment at the time because of the vivid colours. It

THE COMMERCIAL BANK OF SCOTLAND LTD. (contd.)

was designed by Stephen Goodwin, C.B.E., R.A., on one of whose designs the George Medal is based. The principal feature is a portrait of Lord Cockburn, one of the first directors of the bank. A cameo head emblematic of Scotland is supported by figures representing Agriculture and Commerce. The notes have a multi-colour overlay and the cameo head is repeated as a watermark. The back of the £1 note has an elaborate conception of the Arms of the bank. Notes of £5 upwards are of the same general design but for the first time each denomination is in a different basic colour. The main feature of the "large" notes, however, is the very attractive engraving on the back showing the Head Office and surrounding buildings in George Street as they were in the 1840s. The £1 note was issued from 1954 in a new basic colour of blue. Printed signature of General Manager.

1947

53	One Pound	B	Bright purple and multicolour: set 26.
54	One Pound	B	Blue and multicolour: set 27.
55	Five Pounds	X	Bright purple and multicolour:
56	Twenty Pounds	X	Blue and multicolour: set 13.
57	One Hundred Pounds	X	Green and multicolour: set 12.

General Managers: Sir John Maxwell Erskine (later Lord Erskine), until 1953; Ian Wilson Macdonald, from 1954.

Recorded printings of £1 value.

(a) in purple

2 Jan 1947   3 Jan 1949   3 Jan 1950   2 Jan 1951
3 Jan 1952   2 Jan 1953

53

55

(*b*) in blue

2 Jan 1954	3 Jan 1955	2 Jan 1956	2 Jan 1957
2 Jan 1958	1 Jul 1958		

"Specimens" of all denominations exist.

The Company of the Bank of Aberdeen 1798

C. W. Boase in *A Century of Banking in Dundee* states that "In January 1798 a quantity of notes purporting to be guinea notes of the Company of the Bank of Aberdeen were put into circulation. No such bank existed, so they could not be called either forgeries or counterfeit notes". In fact they were entirely bogus.

1

THE COMPANY OF THE BANK OF ABERDEEN (contd.)

1798
  1 **One Guinea**   A   **Bogus note.** Black: uniface
    "One Guinea" at top centre with number (by hand) at left and
    date (also by hand) at right. "Bank of Aberdeen" placed vertically
    at the left of the note. Signed by "Will Cummins" and with ad-
    ditional initials.

John Craw & Company   1760

No information has been forthcoming regarding this Company, described
on the only note seen as "John Craw & Comp. Bankers.", the note having
been issued at Edinburgh.

1760
  1 **Twenty Shillings**   A   Black: uniface
    Portrait of George II contained within the loop of the letter "J" of
    "John Craw & Comp.", the title appearing in Gothic script across
    the top of the note. Bearing an Option Clause ". . . or on the op-
    tion of the said Bankers twenty shillings and sixpence sterling six
    months after the Day of Demand". Dated and numbered by hand.
    "£12 Scots" at top left. Signed by the Manager "By order of the
    Court of Directors" suggesting that this was a joint stock
    enterprise.
    Until something more is known of the status of this bank, the
    possibility that this note is an entirely bogus issue cannot be ruled
    out.

The Cupar Banking Company   1802–1811

Formed at Cupar, Fife, in 1802. It is reported to have retired from business
in 1811 but its affairs were not finally wound up until 1820.

1802
  1 **Twenty Shillings**   A   Black: uniface

GEORGE DEMPSTER & COMPANY
See the Dundee Banking Company.

DENNISTOUN NICHOLSON INGLIS & COMPANY
See the Glasgow Bank Company.

Douglas Heron & Company   1769–1773
The Air (Ayr) Bank

Opened at Ayr on 6 November 1769 with a nominal capital of £150,000. It boasted of a Governor and no fewer than 27 directors acting for the 138 shareholders. Branches were established at Dumfries and Edinburgh. On 12 August 1773 it was resolved to wind up the affairs of the bank. The failure was occasioned by over-trading and by irregularities in the conduct of business, although not of a criminal nature. The circulation at the time of the failure was £220,000.

Few details have been recorded of the notes issued, but one historian remarks "Its notes were printed with types of a peculiar fashion not engraved like other bank notes".

1769
  1 **One Pound**   A   Black: uniface
        Printed by letterpress in a very simple design and in a curious
        "backhand" script. Dated and numbered by hand. Signature of
        Cashier and additionally countersigned.

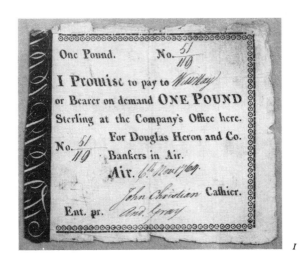

1

DOUGLAS HERON & COMPANY (contd.)

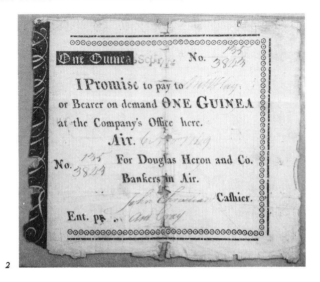

2

2   **One Guinea**   A   Black : uniface
Design and Details similar to those of the £1 note, but "One
Guinea" at top left is in reverse (white-on-black) lettering and date
is handstamped.

SIR WILLIAM DOUGLAS, JOHN NAPIER & COMPANY
See the Galloway Banking Company.

The Dumfries Bank   1766–1772
Alexander Johnston, Hugh Lawson & Company

Opened on 29 October 1766 but transferred the business to Douglas
Heron & Company in 1772 for a consideration of £7,350. It was virtually
insolvent at this time.

1766
1   **One Pound**   A   Black : uniface
A very simple design without any vignette.

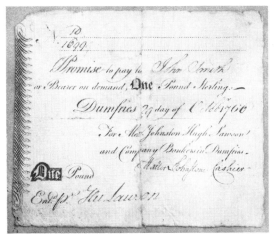

I

2 **Five Pounds**   w   Black: uniface
   No record of other details.
3 **Twenty Pounds**   w
   Similar.

The Dumfries Commercial Bank   1804–1808

Established in 1804 by James Gracie "with the assistance of his son and another partner". It failed in 1808 with a deficiency of 10s. in the £.
   All notes designed and engraved on a copper plate by Kirkwood & Son, Edinburgh.

1804
1 **One Guinea**   A   Black: uniface
   "Dumfries" in Gothic letters in an oblong panel. Dated and numbered by hand. Three signatures.

1805
2 **One Guinea**   A
   Similar, but "One Guinea" to the right of "Dumfries".
3 **Five Pounds**   w   Black: uniface
   Similar general design.

THE DUMFRIES COMMERCIAL BANK (contd.)

2

1808

4   **One Guinea**   A   Black: uniface
    Oval vignette between "One Guinea" and "£1,1– Dumfries".
    Dated and numbered by hand. Two signatures.

4

The Dundee Banking Company   1763–1864
George Dempster & Company

Commenced business in Dundee on 1 August 1763. The note circulation at the outset amounted to £17,936 5s., but eventually reached a peak of £84,968 in 1809. The Dundee New Bank was absorbed on 13 March 1838 (this bank had a circulation of £23,013 at the time). On 20 February 1864, with just over a century of existence, the Dundee Bank was itself absorbed by the Royal Bank of Scotland. The Authorised Circulation under the 1845 Act was £33,451.

IN NAME OF GEORGE DEMPSTER & COMPANY

1763

1　**Five Shillings**　　　　　A　　　Black : uniface
No vignette. With Option Clause reading "On Demand . . . or in the option of the Directors, a note of the Royal Bank or the Bank of Scotland for four of such Notes". Numbered and dated by hand. Payable to Andrew Paterson, and signed by two of the partners.

2　**Ten Shillings**　　　　　A　　　Black : uniface
No vignette. With Option Clause reading "On demand Ten shillings Sterling or in the Option of the Directors Ten shillings and Three pence at the end of six months . . ." Dated and numbered by hand. Payable to Andrew Paterson and signed by two of the partners.
Only one issue of this denomination was made, and only four notes were recorded by the Bank as outstanding in 1770.

3　**One Pound**　　　　　　A　　　Black : uniface
No vignette. With similar Option Clause but reading ". . . or One Pound and sixpence either in Cash or in notes of the Royal Bank or the Bank of Scotland". Signed by the Cashier Robert Jobson and two of the partners.

4　**Five Pounds**　　　　　A
Similar.

1770

5　**One Pound**　　　　　　A　　　Black : uniface
Similar to previous issue but without the Option Clause.

6　**Five Pounds**　　　　　A
Similar.

THE DUNDEE BANKING COMPANY (contd.)

1773

7 **One Pound**   A   Black: uniface
Small vignette of the Arms of Dundee. Dated 6 January 1773.

8 **Five Pounds**   A
Similar.

A contemporary forgery of the £1 note dated 1 August 1777 is
recorded.

IN NAME OF THE DUNDEE BANKING COMPANY

On 13 May 1778 it was decided to order new plates inscribed "The Dundee
Banking Company".

1778

9 **Twenty Shillings**   A   Black: uniface
Similar to the previous issue but inscribed "Dundee Banking
Company".

10 **Five Pounds**   A
Similar.

1797

11 **Five Shillings**   A   Black: uniface
Vignette of heraldic griffin flanked by "Five Shillings" and
"Dundee". Signed by the Cashier. Designed by G. Paton and
engraved on a copper plate by Kirkwood & Son.

On 11 October 1806 it was decided to issue 1 guinea and £20 notes.

1806

12 **One Guinea**   A   Black: uniface

13 **Twenty Pounds**   W   Black: uniface

Later in 1814 £2 notes were added to the range, but neither this nor the 1
guinea note of 1806 proved popular, and in later years the note issue was
restricted to denominations of £1, £5 and £20, although it is possible that a
£100 note was issued in the last year of the Bank's existence.

1816

14 **One Pound**   A   Black: uniface
Circular vignette of the Town Arms flanked by "One Pound" and
"Dundee". Dated and numbered by hand. Payable to William
Webster and signed by the Accountant and Cashier.

14

15   **Five Pounds**   w
     Similar general design.
16   **Twenty Pounds**   w
     Similar.

1845
  17   **One Pound**   A   Black: uniface
       Elaborate vignette of the town Arms flanked by oval panels con-
       taining the word "One". Two allegorical female figures are at left
       and right of the note. Dated by hand but with a printed number.
       Signed by the Cashier and the Accountant. Engraved on steel by
       W. H. Lizars.
       (*a*) With imprint W. H. Lizars.
       (*b*) With imprint W. & A. K. Johnston (1861).
  18   **Five Pounds**   w   Black: uniface
       The Town Arms flanked by rectangular panels containing "Five".
       Figures representing Britannia and Industry appear at left and
       right of the note. Dated by hand but with printed number.
       Engraved on steel by W. H. Lizars.
       (*a*) Imprint W. H. Lizars.
       (*b*) Imprint W. & A. K. Johnston (1861).
       (*c*) With the addition of "Incorporated 1 August 1863" at top of
       the note.
  19   **Twenty Pounds**   w
       Similar.

THE DUNDEE BANKING COMPANY (contd.)

20 **One Hundred Pounds**   w

A proof by W. & A. K. Johnston of this denomination of a similar design to that of the £5 note but with figures representing Industry at the left and of two sailors on the right is in the collection of the Royal Bank of Scotland Ltd. It is inscribed "Incorporated 1 August 1863" so must have been prepared just before the Dundee Bank was taken over by the Royal Bank. The actual issue of this note cannot be confirmed.

Proofs of the other denominations also exist.

A proof of a £1 note designed in an elaborate manner and engraved on steel by J. Fenton, Dundee, is in the collection of the Royal Bank of Scotland Ltd. There is no record of the actual issue of a note of this design.

The Dundee Commercial Bank   1792–1802
(First of this name)

Founded in 1792 but ran into difficulties and was eventually reorganised as the Dundee New Bank on 14 January 1802. The total circulation in 1801 amounted to £113,740

1792
1 Twenty Shillings   A

1797
2 Five Shillings   A

Forgeries of this note were discovered in 1802.

The Dundee Commercial Bank   1825–1838
(Second of this name)

The second Dundee Commercial Bank opened in 1825 with a capital of £50,000 and retired from business in 1838 in favour of the newly established Eastern Bank of Scotland.

I

1825

1 **One Pound**   A   Black and blue: uniface
Large vignette depicting shipping against a background of Dundee
and harbour. Ornate panel in blue containing the legend. Printed
revenue stamp. Dated and numbered by hand. Two signatures.
Designed and engraved by T. Ivory.

Notes of larger denomination were probably issued but no details
have been recorded.

The Dundee New Bank   1802–1838

Formed on 14 January 1802 with a capital of £58,000 to take over the
business of the first Dundee Commercial Bank. The new concern seems to
have made little progress and was purchased by the Dundee Banking Company in 1838. The total circulation in 1810 amounted to £62,355.

1802

1 **One Pound**   A   Black: uniface
2 **Five Pounds**   W   Black: uniface

THE DUNDEE NEW BANK (contd.)

I

The Dundee Union Bank   1809–1844

Commenced business in 1809 with a nominal capital of £100,000. Eight branches were opened in the Dundee area. It was absorbed by the Western Bank of Scotland on 31 March 1844.

1809

1   **Twenty Shillings**   A   Black: uniface
     "Twenty shillings" in Gothic script surrounded by curved scroll-work. Dated and numbered by hand. Two signatures. Water-marked "Dundee Union Bank". Designed and engraved on a copper plate by T. Ivory.

     Forgeries of this note were discovered in 1824.

1823

2   **One Pound**   A   Black: uniface
     Vignette of Steepled building at top left with "One Pound" to the right. Vertical panel of thistles at the left. Dated and numbered by hand and signed by the Cashier and the Accountant. Engraved by Kirkwood & Son.

2

1835

3 **One Pound**   A   Black: uniface
Central Vignette of three female figures (The Three Graces?)
flanked on each side by "One". Elaborate vertical panels at left
and right of the note. Printed revenue stamp on the back. Dated
and numbered by hand and signed by the Cashier and the
Accountant. Engraved on steel by Perkins & Bacon.

COLIN DUNLOP ALEXANDER AND HOUSTON & COMPANY
See the Ship Bank.

DUNLOP HOUSTON GEMMELL & COMPANY
See the Greenock Bank Company.

East Lothian Banking Company   1810–1822

Established at Dunbar with a capital of £80,000. Sir Walter Scott speaks of
it as a company "whose affairs have been very ill-conducted by a villanous
manager". The manager concerned was William Borthwick, who later ab-

EAST LOTHIAN BANKING COMPANY (contd.)

sconded. The bank stopped payment in 1822 with liabilities amounting to
£129,191. These were subsequently paid in full, the Edinburgh private
bank of Sir William Forbes, James Hunter & Co. advancing £100,000 to
assist in that purpose.

All notes bear a small oblong "stamp" with the words "East Lothian
Bank". This was not applied by hand, as would appear, but is actually
lithographed and is identical on each note.

1810

1 **One Guinea**   A   Black: uniface

The vignette at top centre shows two female figures, one bearing a
cornucopia, against a background of Dunbar harbour and flanked
on each side by the words "One" and "Guinea". A panel at the
left shows a sheaf of wheat and a plough. Dated and numbered by
hand. Two signatures. Designed and engraved on a copper plate
by Kirkwood & Son. Watermark "East Lothian Bank".

1821

2 **One Pound**   A   Black: uniface

General design as the foregoing 1 guinea note but with the vignette
flanked by the words "Twenty" and "Shillings". Other details
similar but with printed revenue stamp on the back. Watermark as
before.

2

3

3   **Five Pounds**   w   Black: uniface
General similarity to the £1 note but with the words "Five
Pounds" above the vignette. This note has a curious error, the
spelling of the name of the bank on the left panel reading "East
Lotihan Bank". Dated and numbered by hand. Two signatures.
Printed revenue stamp on the back. Designed and engraved on a
copper plate by Kirkwood & Son.

Unissued notes of all three denominations exist, those of the £1
note being frequently seen.

The Eastern Bank of Scotland   1838–1863

Commenced business at Dundee on 16 July 1838 with a Head Office in the
old Trades Hall there and a second Head Office in Edinburgh, each office
having its own board of directors. This was an ambitious undertaking with
a capital of £1 million. At the outset it accepted a merger with the Dundee
Commercial Bank and a number of branches were opened. It was the first
Scottish bank to designate its principal officer General Manager. In 1844
disagreement between the two boards led to the breakaway of the Edinburgh business under the name of the North British Bank. The Dundee
portion continued to prosper and on 19 January 1863 merged with the
Clydesdale Bank.

THE EASTERN BANK OF SCOTLAND (contd.)

1838

1   **One Pound**   A   Black: uniface
Portrait of Queen Victoria surmounted by a crown. Dated and
numbered by hand. Signatures of General Manager and Accountant. Designed and engraved on steel by J. Fenton, Dundee.

2   **Five Pounds**   w   Black: uniface
Portrait of Queen Victoria with Dundee church at left and Edinburgh Castle at right. The Arms of Dundee and Edinburgh are
also featured. Dated and numbered by hand. Signatures of
General Manager and Accountant. Designed and engraved on
steel by J. Fenton.

3   **Ten Pounds**   w   Black: uniface
General design as £5 note but Arms of the two cities replaced by
cherubs representing Commerce and the Arts. The royal portrait is
flanked by figures "10" in ornate style. Dated and numbered by
hand. Signatures of General Manager and Accountant. Designed
and engraved on steel by J. Fenton.

A later issue, similar in all respects to the above, has the figures of
value flanking the portrait replaced by words "TEN POUNDS".

4   **Twenty Pounds**   w   Black: uniface
Similar to the first issue of the £10 note. Designed and engraved by
J. Fenton.

1850

5   **One Pound**   A   Black: uniface
Arms of Dundee and Edinburgh supported by Neptune (left) and
female figure representing Agriculture (right) against a
background of the entrance to Dundee Harbour and Edinburgh
Castle. Vignettes featuring a sailor with sextant and an allegorical
figure of Commerce are at the left and right of the note respectively. At the bottom of the note is an illustration of the Trades
Hall in which the Dundee Head Office was situated. Dated and
numbered by hand. Signatures of General Manager and Accountant. Engraved on steel by W. H. Lizars, Edinburgh.

6   **Five Pounds**   w   Black: uniface
Arms of Edinburgh and Dundee supported by Commerce and
Neptune in reversed positions to the £1 note. Vignette of farmer
leading a horse and Commerce at left and right of the note. Dated
and numbered by hand. Signatures of General Manager and Accountant. Engraved on steel by W. H. Lizars.

5

1861

7 **One Pound** A Black: uniface

Design as in the 1850 £1 note but modified to include the words "Pursuant to Act 16 & 17 Victoria Cap.63" at top of the note. Other details as before but now bearing the printers' imprint W. & A. K. Johnston, Edinburgh.

Proofs exist of all the above notes.

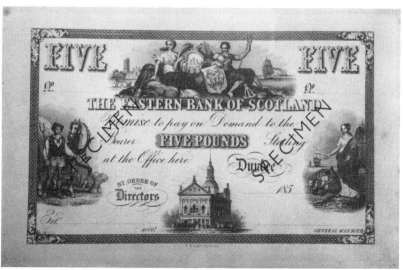

6

The Edinburgh and Glasgow Bank   1844–1858

Created on 17 January 1844 by the amalgamation of the Edinburgh and Leith Bank and the Glasgow Joint Stock Bank. There were two boards, one in Edinburgh and the other in Glasgow. The Authorised Circulation amounted to £136,657. The Bank never enjoyed a full measure of public confidence and after several attempts to secure a merger it was taken over by the Clydesdale Bank on 21 June 1858, 19 out of the 27 branches being retained by that Bank.

All notes were designed and engraved by W. & A. K. Johnston whose founder, William Johnston, became chairman of the Bank in 1849.

1844

1   **One Pound**   A   Black with mauve border
Central vignette of a shield bearing the Arms of Edinburgh and Glasgow in alternate quarters and supported by allegorical figures representing Commerce and Agriculture (left) and Industry in the form of Neptune (right). Dated and numbered by hand: one signature. The back has an ornate design incorporating the initials of the Bank and the Arms of the two cities.

3

2   **Five Pounds**   w   Black
    Similar in general design to the £1 note, the vignette being flanked
    on either side by the value "Five". Dated and numbered by hand.
    Two signatures.

3   **Ten Pounds**   w   Black
    Similar in design to the £5 note.

1852

4   **Five Pounds**   w   Black
    General design as the previous £5 note but with a new panel on the
    left bearing a lion rampant. The vignette is flanked by the words
    "Five" on which the figure 5 is superimposed. "Pursuant to Act of
    Parliament etc." is added underneath the vignette.

The Edinburgh and Leith Bank   1839–1844

Opened for business on 2 January 1839 and had a number of branches in
the south-east of Scotland. It absorbed the Southern Bank of Scotland in
1840 and in 1844 joined with the Glasgow Joint Stock Bank to form the
Edinburgh and Glasgow Bank.

1839

1   **One Pound**   A   Black: uniface
    Vignette of Britannia in a central position flanked by female
    figures representing Agriculture and Commerce. Edinburgh Castle
    and the Port of Leith form the background. Dated and numbered
    by hand. Signed on behalf of the Manager and the Accountant.
    Engraved on steel by W. & A. K. Johnston.

2   **One Guinea**   A   Black: uniface
    Vignette similar to that in the £1 note but the background now
    features the Royal Scottish Academy and the Customs House at
    Leith. Other details as in the £1 note.

    This note has been seen in proof form only, and it is not certain
    that a note of 1 guinea denomination was issued at such a late
    date.

3   **Five Pounds**   w   Black: uniface
    Arms of Edinburgh and Leith supported by Agriculture and
    Commerce. Dated and numbered by hand. Signatures of Manager
    and Accountant. Engraved on steel by W. & A. K. Johnston.

4   **Ten Pounds**   w   Black: uniface
    Similar to the £5 note but the vignette is flanked on either side by
    the words "Ten". Other details as before.

THE EDINBURGH AND LEITH BANK (*contd.*)

2

5 **Twenty Pounds**   w   Black: uniface
   Similar to the above but the vignette is flanked by "£20" in figures.

6 **One Hundred Pounds**   w   Black: uniface
   Similar, but the vignette is flanked on either side by "£100"
   in figures.

Proofs in various colour combinations exist of the £20 and £100
notes but it is considered unlikely that these denominations were
issued other than in black.
Proofs in black exist of all denominations.
Leith was incorporated by the city of Edinburgh in 1922.

The Falkirk Banking Company   1782–1825

Established in 1782 and had a successful career in the Falkirk district.
When it was wound up in 1825 each £100 share was worth £1,500.

1782

1 **One Pound**   A   Black: uniface

1797

2 **Five Shillings**   A   Black: uniface
   Small oval vignette of Falkirk High Church. Printed date (6 April).
   Numbered by hand. Two signatures. Payable to Alex. Callander.

The Falkirk Union Banking Company   1803–1816

Commenced business in 1803 with a capital of £12,000 held by 14 partners. Sequestrated on 18 October 1816 with liabilities amounting to £60,000. This failure was one of the rare occasions in Scottish banking history where the noteholders were not paid in full.

1803

1   **Twenty Shillings**   A   Black: uniface
    Oval vignette of standing female figure and including a thistle and a ship, flanked by "One Pound Sterling" and "Ll Falkirk". Dated and numbered by hand. Two signatures. Impressed revenue stamp. Engraved on a copper plate by Kirkwood & Son. Paper manufacturers' watermark.

2   **One Guinea**   A   Black: uniface
    Floral vignette consisting of a thistle, rose and shamrock intertwined and bearing the motto "Trio juncta in Uno". Dated and numbered by hand. Two signatures. Designed by G. Paton and printed on wove paper from a copper plate engraved by Kirkwood & Son. No watermark.

3   **Five Pounds**   W   Black: uniface
    General design as No. 2.

4   **Twenty Pounds**   W   Black: uniface
    Similar.

I

I

The Fife Banking Company   1802–1829

Founded at Cupar in 1802 with a capital of £30,000 but was grossly mis-
managed. It closed its doors on 21 May 1829 but final settlement of all its
affairs was held up until 1850, all debts being paid in full.

1808
  1 **One Pound**   A   Black: uniface
     Central vignette of a knight in armour and on horseback with the
     inscription "Thane of Fife". Numbered and dated by hand. Two
     signatures. Printed revenue stamp on back on notes issued after
     1820. Designed and engraved by Kirkwood & Son. Paper manufac-
     turers' watermark.

Sir William Forbes, James Hunter & Company
                                            1773–1838

Compared with England, Scotland had relatively few private banks: the
system of setting up larger joint stock companies was preferred. This bank
was undoubtedly the most famous of the private banks. It originated from
the mercantile firm of John Coutts & Co., which was in business in 1723,
but in consequence of a quarrel with Coutts & Co. of London (founded by
the sons of the first John Coutts), the name was changed on 1 January 1773

to Sir William Forbes, James Hunter & Co. This was a highly respected firm which merged with the Glasgow Union Bank in 1838, carrying on business under its own name until 1843 when the Union Bank of Scotland was created. The circulation in 1782 was £82,750 but this figure rose to £251,400 in 1810.

Prior to 1782 this bank issued the notes of the Royal Bank of Scotland.

1782

1   **One Guinea**   A   Black: uniface
   Oval vignette of Parliament Close, Edinburgh, with "One Guinea" in ornate letters on the right. Printed date (1 July 1781). Numbered by hand. Two signatures. Designed by a Mr. Butterworth and engraved by Robert Kirkwood – the first note to be engraved by him and the forerunner of the many fine engravings by the firm which he founded.

2   **Five Pounds**   W   Black: uniface
   Details and design similar to the 1 guinea note. Both notes payable to Lewis Hay.

   Although dated 1 July 1781 these notes were not issued until 1 January 1782. It was not realised at first that 1 July 1781 was a Sunday and doubts were therefore raised as to their validity. They were immediately replaced by notes dated 1 March 1782.

1808

3   **Twenty Shillings**   A   Black: uniface
   Square vignette of Parliament Close flanked by words "Twenty" and "Shillings". Printed date (3 Novr.). Hand numbered. Payable

3

SIR WILLIAM FORBES, JAMES HUNTER & COMPANY (contd.)

4

to Patrick Sanderson. Two signatures. Designed and engraved by Kirkwood & Son.

4   **Five Pounds**   W   Black and red: uniface
Oval vignette of Parliament Close in red at top left with "Five Pounds" in large ornate letters, also in red, to the right. Printed date, numbered by hand. Payable to Patrick Sanderson. Printed revenue stamp on back of later issues. Watermarked "Sir William Forbes J. Hunter & Co." Signed on behalf of the Firm with one additional signature. Designed by Butterworth and engraved by Kirkwood & Son.

1820

5   **One Pound**   A   Black: uniface
Square vignette of Parliament Close with equestrian statue in foreground and flanked by "One" and "Pound". Dated and numbered by hand. Payable to Robert Borrowman. Signed on behalf of the Firm with one additional signature. Watermarked "Sir William Forbes J. Hunter & Co." Engraved by Kirkwood & Son.
Contemporary forgeries of this note exist.

5

1824

6   **One Guinea**   A   Black : uniface

Oval vignette of Parliament Close with statue in foreground at top left, "One Guinea' in ornate letters to the right. Dated and numbered by hand. Payable to Robert Borrowman. Printed revenue stamp on back. Watermarked "Sir William Forbes J. Hunter & Co.". Signed on behalf of the Firm with one additional signature.

The Galloway Banking Company   1806–1821
Sir William Douglas, John Napier & Company

Founded at Castle Douglas in 1806. After a career of some fifteen years it withdrew from business in 1821 through a bad debt of £55,000 with a firm of cattle-drovers.

1806

1   **One Pound**   A   Black : uniface

Arms of Castle Douglas at top left. Dated and numbered by hand. Signatures of Manager and Cashier. Payable to James Hannay. Designed and engraved by Kirkwood & Son.
Unissued notes exist.

THE GALLOWAY BANKING COMPANY (contd.)

I

2 **Five Pounds**   w   Black: uniface
   The vignette of the Arms of Castle Douglas is in a central position
   and flanked by the words "Five Pounds" and "Castle Douglas".
   Dated and numbered by hand. Signatures of Manager and
   Cashier. Payable to James Hannay. Engraved by Kirkwood & Son.

2

1807

3 **One Guinea**   A   Black: uniface

Vignette as before but flanked by "One Guinea" and "£1–1/–Ster, Castle Douglas". Payable to James Hannay and signed by the Manager and the Cashier. Designed and engraved by Kirkwood & Son.

Unissued notes exist.

The Glasgow and Ship Bank   1836–1843

This bank was formed by the merger of the Ship Bank and the Glasgow Bank Company in 1836 and seven years later was itself merged in the Union Bank of Scotland, which used the Glasgow and Ship building for its first Head Office.

1836

1 **One Pound**   A   Black: uniface

Central vignette of the tree, fish and bell of the Glasgow Arms against a background of the City and flanked by oval panels containing "One". Vertical panel at left containing vignette of sailing ship. Dated and numbered by hand and signed by the Cashier and the Accountant. Printed revenue stamp on back. Engraved on steel plate by Perkins & Bacon.

I

THE GLASGOW AND SHIP BANK (contd.)

2 **Five Pounds**   w   Black: uniface
   Similar general design to that of the £1 note but sailing ship
   appears on the panel at the right. Other details similar.

3 **Twenty Pounds**   w
   Similar.

4 **One Hundred Pounds**   w
   Similar.

The design of these notes departs considerably from Scottish
traditional lines, being extremely complex and "busy" and with
little artistic merit.

Proofs of the £1 and £100 notes exist.

The Glasgow Arms Bank   1750–1793
Cochrane Murdoch & Company 1750
Murdoch Robertson & Company 1782

Opened in Glasgow on 6 November 1750 with a measure of support from
the Royal Bank of Scotland, its name being derived from the fact that it
featured the Arms of Glasgow on its notes. Its progress was never spec-
tacular and it closed its doors in 1793, all creditors being paid in full.

1750

  1 **Twenty Shillings**   A   Black: uniface

Arms of Glasgow at top left. Dated and numbered by hand and signed by Archibald Cochrane and John Murdoch together with the Cashier.

1771

  2 **One Guinea**   A   Black: uniface

Small circular vignette of the Arms of Glasgow at top centre. Dated and numbered by hand. Signatures of one partner and the Cashier.

The Glasgow Bank Company   1809–1836
Dennistoun Nicholson Inglis & Co.

Established 1809 as a private bank and soon met with success. The note circulation increased from £89,847 in June 1811 to £153,920 in 1819. It merged with the Ship Bank of Carrick Brown & Company in 1836 to form a public bank under the name Glasgow and Ship Bank.

1809

  1 **One Pound**   A   Black: uniface

Small rectangular panel bearing the initials of the partnership in ornamental letters flanked by the words "One Pound" and "Glasgow". Dated and numbered by hand. Signatures of the Cashier and the Accountant. Engraved on a copper plate by Haldane.

Contemporary forgery dated 10 May 1819 known.

I

THE GLASGOW BANK COMPANY (contd.)

2

1830

2 **One Pound**   A   Black, with brown border: uniface
Arms of Glasgow flanked by words "One Pound" and "Glasgow".
Dated and numbered by hand. Signed by the Cashier and the Ac-
countant. Engraved on a steel plate by Haldane.

3 **One Pound**   A   Black, brown and blue: uniface

As No. 2 but with addition of an ornamental panel in blue across
the centre of the design.

3

THE GLASGOW CITY BANK
See the City Banking Company of Glasgow – not to be confused with the City of Glasgow Bank.

The Glasgow Joint Stock Bank 1840–1844

Opened for business on 3 November 1840 with a nominal capital of £1¼ million. It was a single-office bank but had a considerable business. On 17 January 1844 after a life of just over three years it merged with the Edinburgh and Leith Bank to form the Edinburgh and Glasgow Bank.

1840

1 **One Pound**   A   Black: uniface

Vignette showing the River God in the form of Neptune against a background of shipping on the Clyde. Statues of female figures holding vases on their heads and standing on plinths bearing the City Arms are at left and right of the note. Dated and numbered by hand. Signatures of Manager and Accountant. Engraved on steel by Joseph Swan, Glasgow.

Although the bank must have had a considerable circulation only two of these notes appear to have survived.

A proof of a £1 note with a vignette of Britannia seated and front-facing flanked by "One Pound" on either side is known. It bears

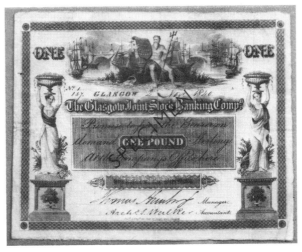

I

THE GLASGOW JOINT STOCK BANK (contd.)

no engravers' imprint but appears to be from a steel plate. This must be considered an "essay" as no note of this design was issued. It is almost certain that notes of larger denomination(s) were issued but no record or details have been seen.

THE GLASGOW MERCHANT BANK
See the Merchant Banking Company of Glasgow

THE GLASGOW SHIP BANK
See The Ship Bank.

The Glasgow Union Banking Company 1830–1843

Formed in 1830 this was the immediate predecessor of the Union Bank of Scotland. Within a few years it had absorbed the Thistle Bank, also Sir William Forbes, James Hunter & Co. and the Paisley Union Bank. In 1843 the title was changed to the more appropriate and national one of the Union Bank of Scotland.

1830

1   **One Pound**   A   Black: uniface

An elaborate design from a steel plate engraved by W. H. Lizars, the main feature being an equestrian statue at top centre flanked by

I

2

"One Pound" and "Glasgow". Three other vignettes are in oval frames across the centre of the design, the central one featured a portrait of William IV. Dated and numbered by hand and signed by the Accountant and the Cashier. Printed revenue stamp on back.

2   **Five Pounds**   w   Black: uniface
    Similar general design to that of the £1 note but omitting the vignettes across the centre. Other details as before.

3   **Twenty Pounds**   w   Black: uniface
    Design similar to that of the £1 note and including the central vignettes. Other details similar.

Proofs of all three values are known with and without the manuscript endorsement "Specimen".

The Greenock Bank Company   1785–1843
The Greenock Banking Company
Dunlop Houston Gemmell & Company

Founded at Greenock in 1785 it was absorbed by the Western Bank of Scotland in November 1843. At that time it was the last private bank existing in Scotland. It was also the scene of an historic robbery on 9 March 1828.

THE GREENOCK BANK COMPANY (contd.)

1785

   1 **One Guinea**   A   Black: uniface

       The central vignette illustrates an oak tree with a ship in the background and flanked by the words "One" and "Guinea" in Gothic script. Dated and numbered by hand and bearing two signatures. Engraved on a copper plate by Robert Kirkwood.

1820

   2 **Five Pounds**   W   Black: uniface

       Design, similar to that of the 1 guinea note, is by G. Paton and the note is printed from a copper plate engraved by Kirkwood & Son. Dated and numbered by hand and signed by the Cashier and one other.

   3 **Twenty Pounds**   W   Black: uniface

       Similar to the £5 note.

1825

   4 **One Pound**   A   Black and green: uniface

       Small circular vignette of oak tree printed in green and set in a panel showing the estuary of the Clyde, this panel extending the whole width of the note. A vertical panel at the left is also in green. Dated and numbered by hand and signed by the Cashier and one other. Printed revenue stamp on back. Designed and engraved by Kirkwood & Son.

4

A genuine note in spite of the manuscript inscription "Forged".

1838

5   **One Pound**   A   Black: uniface

Engraving showing the port of Greenock with an early steam vessel in the foreground. The vignette is flanked by "One Pound" and "Greenock". Dated and numbered by hand and bearing two signatures. Printed from a steel plate, the engraver of which is unknown.

Proofs of this note exist.

The Greenock Union Bank   1840–1844

Formed in 1840 with a paid-up capital of £125,000, the shares, however, soon falling to a discount. Its career seems to have been spent courting the Western Bank of Scotland and the Clydesdale Bank, ultimately joining the latter in 1844.

1840

1   **One Pound**   A   Black: uniface

2   **Five Pounds**   W   Black: uniface

Other details are not on record.

HAY & OGILVIE
See the Shetland Bank.

Hunters & Company   1773–1843

Founded in Ayr in 1773 with a capital of £10,000 by James Hunter, the Cashier of the ill-fated firm of Douglas Heron & Company. It was a well-managed bank and had a successful career independent of both the Edinburgh and Glasgow banking groups. The note circulation in 1777 amounted to £42,000. In 1821 the Kilmarnock Bank was taken over and Hunters eventually merged with the Union Bank of Scotland in 1843 at which time it had seven branches in the County.

HUNTERS & COMPANY (contd.)

1773

  1 **One Guinea**   A   Black: uniface
      Vignette consisting of the King's head. Dated and numbered by
      hand. Watermarked. Vignette shows obverse and reverse of the
      current gold guinea piece.

  2 **Five Pounds**   W   Black: uniface
      Similar general design to that of the 1 guinea note.
      There was a contemporary forgery of the 1 guinea note dated 1
      August 1781.

3

1828

  3 **One Pound**   A   Black and brick red: uniface
      Medallion with St. George and the Dragon surmounted by
      "Twenty Shillings" in curved letters, all in brick red. Vertical panel
      of thistles at left. Dated and numbered by hand and with three
      signatures. Printed revenue stamp on back. Designed by Taylor
      and engraved by Kirkwood & Son.
      Unissued notes endorsed "Specimen" by hand exist.

Inglis Borthwick Gilchrist & Company 1805–1815
James Inglis & Co. 1815–1834

This private bank opened at Edinburgh in 1805. The firm failed in 1834 with liabilities amounting to £23,000. The note circulation was not large.

1805

1   **One Pound**   A   Black: uniface
Oval vignette of the Arms of Edinburgh flanked by "One" and "Pound". The remainder of the note contains the legend in a dignified "copper plate" script. Dated and numbered by hand. Signed in the firm's name with one additional signature. Payable to James Roberts.

1809

2   **One Guinea**   A   Black: uniface
Arms of Edinburgh surmounted by "One Guinea" in curved letters. Dated and numbered by hand. Signed in the firm's name with one additional signature. Payable to James Roberts. Designed by G. Butterworth and engraved on a copper plate by J. Burns.

ALEXANDER JOHNSTON, HUGH LAWSON & COMPANY
See the Dumfries Bank

George Keller & Company 1764–1765

This firm were not bankers but wine and spirit merchants, who traded in Glasgow in 1764 and who in common with a number of other traders issued notes. These circulated as far as Aberdeen where they were reported to have been dishonoured. They are not strictly "bank" notes but are listed here as one example of the note-issuing mania of the period which was brought under control by the Act of 1765.

1764

1   **Five Shillings**   120 × 90 mm   Black: uniface
No vignette. Dated and numbered by hand. Signed in the firm's name.

GEORGE KELLER & COMPANY (contd.)

3

2   **Ten Shillings** 125 × 90 mm   Black: uniface
    £6 Scots
    No vignette. Dated and numbered by hand. Signed in the firm's
    name. Inscribed "for value received in goods £6 Scots."

3   **Twenty Shillings**   A   Black: uniface
    £12 Scots
    Small vignette of clasped hands. Dated and numbered by hand.
    Signed in the firm's name. Inscribed payable "on demand . . . or
    in the option of our Cashier . . . in an Edinburgh or Glasgow Bank
    Note. Value received in goods £12 Scots."

The Kilmarnock Bank   1802–1821
The Kilmarnock Banking Company

Established on 10 June 1802. It had a fairly successful but strictly local
business. In October 1821 it was absorbed by Hunters & Company of Ayr.

1802

1   **One Guinea**   A   Black: uniface
    Arms of Kilmarnock flanked by "One Guinea" and "Kilmar-
    nock". Dated and numbered by hand and bearing three
    signatures. Designed by J. Sanderson and engraved on a copper
    plate by Kirkwood & Son.

I

2   **Two Guineas**   A   Black: uniface
Arms of Kilmarnock flanked by panels containing words "Two"
and "Guineas". Dated and numbered by hand and bearing three
signatures. Designed by J. Sanderson and engraved by Kirkwood &
Son.

Leith Banking Company   1793–1842

Founded on 1 January 1793, this bank had seven branches including one at
Carlisle which actually registered as an English bank! It was sequestrated in
1842 with debts of £123,582 on which dividends totalling 13s. 4d. in the £
were paid. At the time of its failure it had a note circulation of about
£10,000.

1793
1   **Twenty Shillings**   A   Black: uniface
Oval vignette of ship entering the Port of Leith flanked by
"Twenty" and "Shillings" Dated and numbered by hand and
signed by the Manager and Cashier.

1798
2   **One Guinea**   A   Black: uniface
Similar vignette to that of the 20s. note but placed top left with
"One Guinea" at the right. Printed date 1 January 1798 and
numbered by hand. Signed by the Manager and the Cashier.
Designed by G. Paton and engraved on a copper plate by J. Beugo.

LEITH BANKING COMPANY (contd.)

2

3   **Two Pounds**   A   Black: uniface
    Octagonal vignette of sailing ship flanked by panels containing
    words "Two" and "Pounds". Payable to Alex. Alison and dated
    and numbered by hand.

4   **Twenty Pounds**   W   Black: uniface
    Similar oval vignette to that on the 20s. note. Payable to James Ker
    and dated and numbered by hand. Signed by the Manager and the
    Accountant and also by James Ker. Engraved by J. Beugo.

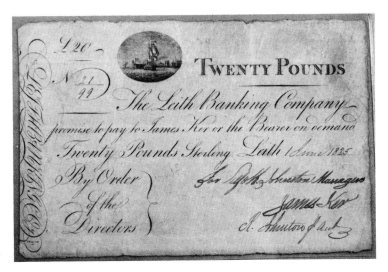

4

1817

5   **One Guinea**   A   Black: uniface
"One Guinea" in Gothic letters flanked by two vignettes of shipping entering Leith (left) and of a local building (right). Dated and
numbered by hand and signed on behalf of the Manager and the
Cashier. Designed by J. McNaughton and printed from a copper
plate engraved by John Beugo.
(*a*) Payable to Alexander Alison.
(*b*) Payable to Alexander Macdonald.

1824

6   **Twenty Shillings**   A   Black: uniface
The vignette shows the arrival of George IV at the Port of Leith on
the occasion of the State Visit to Edinburgh. Dated and numbered
by hand and signed on behalf of the Accountant and the Cashier.
Printed revenue stamp on the back. Engraved on steel by Perkins &
Heath.
(*a*) Payable to Alexander Macdonald.
(*b*) Payable to Henry Johnston.

7   **One Guinea**   A   Black: uniface
The central vignette illustrates the arrival on shore of George IV
on the occasion of the State Visit, and this is flanked by smaller
vignettes of a portrait of the King (left) and of the Arms of Leith
(right). Dated and numbered by hand and signed on behalf of the
Manager and the Cashier. Engraved on steel by Perkins & Heath.

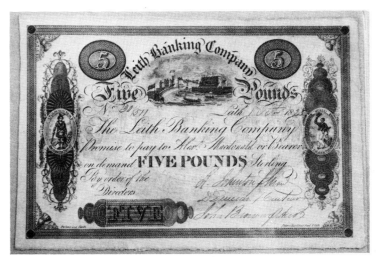

8

LEITH BANKING COMPANY (contd.)

8   **Five Pounds**   W   Black: uniface
    Vignette as on the 20s. note but flanked by oval panels containing
    the figure "5". Dated and numbered by hand and signed on behalf
    of the Manager, the Cashier, and the Accountant. Engraved on
    steel by Perkins & Heath.

John Maberly & Company   1818–1832
Aberdeen, Montrose, Dundee, Edinburgh & Glasgow
Exchange & Deposit Banks

In spite of the lengthy title this was not a bank in the true sense. John
Maberly & Company were English linen manufacturers, registered in
England, but having spinning mills in Scotland. The "banking" side of the
business was established in 1818 in order to profit by the high London
rates of exchange. The notes were first payable in London but later in
Edinburgh. The town of issue is inserted by hand to the left of the date. In
1832 they failed, with debts of £149,082 and paying a dividend of only
4s. 5d. in the £.

1818
    1   **One Pound**   A   Black: uniface
        Central vignette of Arms framed in a semi-circle by "Exchange &
        Deposit Banks". Numbered and dated by hand with the place of

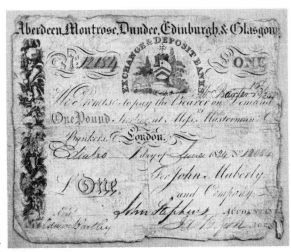

2

issue also inserted by hand. Signed by the Accountant and the Agent. Engraved by W. & I. Thorogood, London. Instructions regarding the presentation of the note are contained in seven lines of small print at the bottom left corner of the note.

1823

2   **One Pound**   A   Black: uniface
Similar to the previous note but the clause containing instructions on presentation is now replaced by a third signature.

1825

3   **One Pound**   A   Black
Back printed in black and blue. Identical design as the foregoing but engraved on steel by Perkins & Heath, London. The back is printed with an ornamental framework with small oval panels containing the word "One" in blue. The framework accommodates the printed revenue stamp.

Notes Nos. 1–3 are all payable at the office of Masterman & Co. Bankers, London.

1828

4   **One Pound**   A   Black
Back in black and blue. Similar to the previous note. Payable in Edinburgh.

£5 notes are reported to have been prepared but it is certain that they were never issued.

John McAdam & Company   1763–1771

Established as a private firm at Ayr in 1763. In 1771 it was purchased by Douglas Heron & Company for the sum of £18,000.

1763

1   **Five Shillings** 130 × 75 mm   Black: uniface
Portrait of George III at top left. Dated and numbered by hand and having three signatures.

2   **Ten Shillings** 150 × 80 mm   Black: uniface
Similar in design to the 5s. note.

Only three notes of this bank are recorded as having survived.

JOHN McADAM & COMPANY (contd.)

McKEITH RINTOUL & COMPANY
See the Perth United Company.

J. Stewart Mackenzie   1823–1826
Stornoway

This note is frequently listed under the heading "Stornoway Bank", but there was no bank in Stornoway until 1830. The notes, a number of which appear to have survived, are purely a private issue by J. Stewart Mackenzie, husband of Lady Hood Mackenzie, the proprietrix of the Island of Lewis. Graham states that "if any of those notes travelled eastward they were retired by the Commercial Bank in Inverness", but this fact cannot be confirmed.

I

1823

  1   **One Pound**   A   Black: uniface
Vignette of sailing ship above "Stornaway" in a rectangular panel.
That Stornoway should be mis-spelt is rather surprising. Dated
and numbered by hand. Printed revenue stamp on the back.
Engraved on steel by Rowe, Change Alley, London.

MANSFIELD HUNTER & COMPANY
See Ramsays Bonars & Company.

MANSFIELD RAMSAY & COMPANY
See Ramsays Bonars & Company.

SIR JAMES MAXWELL, JOHN RITCHIE & COMPANY
See the Thistle Bank.

THE MERCHANT BANK OF STIRLING
See Stirling Merchant Banking Company.

The Merchant Banking Company of Glasgow
1769–1793
The Glasgow Merchant Bank

Founded by smaller traders in Glasgow in 1769. It failed in 1774 but the
creditors were paid in full and the business was re-started. It finally
collapsed in 1793.

1772

  1   **One Pound**   A   Black: uniface
Vignette containing a globe at top left with a small medallion containing a monogram adjacent to it at the right. Printed date 1 October 1772. Numbered by hand and with two signatures.

The Montrose Bank
The Montrose Banking Company

1814–1829

A small bank established at Montrose in May 1814 with a capital of £15,000. After an uneventful career of fifteen years it merged with the Dundee Union Bank in 1829.

1814

1   **One Pound**   A   Black: uniface
     Arms of the town of Montrose at top left with "One Pound" in a panel at the right. Printed date 2 May 1814 but numbered by hand. Signed by the Cashier and the Accountant. Printed revenue stamp on the back. Designed and engraved by T. Ivory.

2   **One Guinea**   A   Black: uniface
     Arms of Montrose at top left with "One Guinea" within a series of curves at the right. Dated and numbered by hand and signed by the Cashier and the Accountant. Embossed revenue stamp. Designed and engraved by T. Ivory.

2

1818

3 **Five Pounds** w Black: uniface

Arms of Montrose at top left with "Five Pounds" in a large oblong panel at the right. Dated and numbered by hand and signed by the Cashier and the Accountant. Designed and engraved by T. Ivory.

Only one of the £5 notes has been seen, this bearing the date 31 July 1818. They may have been issued at an earlier date.

MOORES CARRICK & COMPANY
See the Ship Bank.

MURDOCH ROBERTSON & COMPANY
See the Glasgow Arms Bank.

SIR WILLIAM NAPIER & COMPANY
See the Renfrewshire Banking Company.

The National Bank of Scotland 1825–1959
The National Bank of Scotland Limited

Constituted on 21 March 1825 with an authorised capital of £5 million. It opened for business in Edinburgh on 30 October of that year, having purchased a hotel in St. Andrew Square now the site of the Head Office of the Royal Bank of Scotland Limited. From its inception it adopted the policy of a branch system and opened throughout the country. On 5 August 1831 the Bank was granted its Royal Charter of Incorporation and in 1864 was the first of the Scottish Banks to open in London. The Commercial Banking Company of Aberdeen was absorbed in 1833 and the Perth Union Bank in 1836. On 3 April 1882 it registered under the Companies Act of 1879 adding the word "Limited" to its title. In 1918 an offer by Lloyds Bank Ltd. to purchase the whole of the capital was accepted, and in 1959 it merged with the Commercial Bank of Scotland Limited to form National Commercial Bank of Scotland Limited. The Authorised Circulation was £297,024 and the actual circulation around £15,000,000 at the time of the merger.

THE NATIONAL BANK OF SCOTLAND (contd.)

The first issue was dated 11 October 1825 and consisted of no less than six denominations. They were all printed in black and uniface, of the same basic design and differing only in size and in minor details. This design consists of a representation of the Royal Arms surmounted by St. Andrew and Cross, and flanked by panels containing the value. In the 1 guinea note the Arms are flanked by the words "One" and "Guinea" in rectangular panels. All notes are hand dated and numbered and bear signatures on behalf of the Manager and the Accountant. Printed from plates engraved on steel by Perkins & Bacon, London.

1825

1	**One Pound**	A	Black: uniface
2	**One Guinea** Similar.	A	
3	**Five Pounds** Similar.	W	
4	**Ten Pounds** Similar.	W	
5	**Twenty Pounds** Similar.	W	
6	**One Hundred Pounds** Similar.	W	

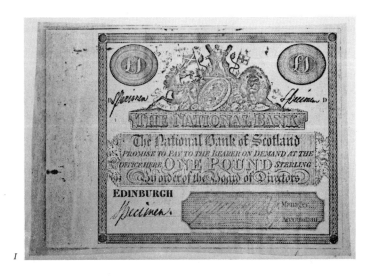

I

The Bank having been granted its Royal Charter in 1831, the plates were modified to include "Incorporated by Royal Charter" under the Royal Arms. Included in the top border are the words "Under Act 16 & 17 Vict. Cap. 68". All other details as in the first issue. Guinea notes were now discontinued.

1831
7	**One Pound**	A	Black: uniface
8	**Five Pounds**	W	
	Similar.		
9	**Ten Pounds**	W	
	Similar.		
10	**Twenty Pounds**	W	
	Similar.		
11	**One Hundred Pounds**	W	
	Similar.		

As an additional security against photographic forgery a lithographed panel in red containing the value of the note was added in 1862, the basic plate still being printed in black. The date and number are now printed but other details remain as before.

1862
12	**One Pound**	A	Black and red: uniface
13	**Five Pounds**	W	
	Similar.		

12

THE NATIONAL BANK OF SCOTLAND (contd.)

14   **Twenty Pounds**   w   Black and red: uniface
        Similar.
15   **One Hundred Pounds**   w
        Similar.

In 1882 the Bank registered under the Companies Act of 1879 and new plates were prepared adding the word "Limited" to the title. The panel under the Royal Arms now reads "Incorporated by Royal Charter and Act of Parliament". "Edinburgh" and the date are in larger characters but other details remain as in the previous issue.

1882
  16   **One Pound**   A   Black and red: uniface
          (*a*) Numbered in red (1882).
          (*b*) Numbered in black (1889).
  17   **Five Pounds**   w   Black and red: uniface
  18   **Twenty Pounds**   w
          Similar.
  19   **One Hundred Pounds**   w
          Similar.

The same basic designs having been in use for almost 70 years, entirely new plates were prepared in 1893 by Waterlow & Sons Ltd. with the most elaborate engraving of any Scottish note. They represent the highest achievement of security printers of the period, although the artistic merits of the design suffer from its ornateness. The general design, which is common to all denominations, features the Royal Arms in a central position surmounted by the Bank's title in curved lettering. To the left is a portrait designated the "Marquess of Lothian K.T. Governor of the Bank", while the corresponding panel on the right shows Edinburgh Castle. Smaller panels at the bottom of the note feature shipping on the Clyde (left) and the Palace of Holyroodhouse (right). The back has a view of Princes Street, Edinburgh, and the Castle looking westwards from Calton Hill and contained within a large area of intricate engine work. Printed in blue from the engraved plate and with a yellow and red lithographic overlay in the form of a sunburst in the £1 note and a discreet floral design in the higher denominations. The £20 and £100 notes have an additional overlay in pink. Printed signature on behalf of the Manager and signed by hand on behalf of the Accountant. Engraved by Waterlow & Sons Ltd.

20

1893

20	**One Pound**	A	Blue, yellow and red
21	**Five Pounds** Similar.	W	
22	**Twenty Pounds**	W	Blue, yellow, red and pink
23	**One Hundred Pounds** Similar.	W	

All denominations are known overprinted "specimen" in red.

Small modifications were made to the plates in 1908, the caption under the portrait now reading "The Most Honble. the Marquess of Lothian K.T. Governor of the Bank 1874–1900" in two lines. Both signatures are now printed being those of the *General* Manager and the Accountant. Other details remain as before.

1908

24	**One Pound**	A	Blue, yellow and red
25	**Five Pounds** Similar.	W	
26	**Twenty Pounds**	W	Blue, yellow, red and pink
27	**One Hundred Pounds** Similar.	W	

THE NATIONAL BANK OF SCOTLAND (contd.)

Recorded printings of the £1 note

11 Nov 1910	15 May 1911	11 Nov 1912	15 May 1913
11 Nov 1913	15 May 1914	1 Aug 1914	1 Oct 1915
11 Nov 1915	15 May 1916	11 Nov 1916	15 May 1917
12 Nov 1917	15 May 1918	11 Nov 1918	15 May 1919
11 Nov 1919	24 May 1920	11 Nov 1920	11 Nov 1922
15 May 1923	15 May 1924		

In 1925 the printed signature of the General Manager was replaced by that of the Cashier, other details remaining unchanged.

1925

28	**One Pound**	A	Blue, yellow and red.
29	**Five Pounds** Similar.	W	
30	**Twenty Pounds**	W	Blue, yellow, red and pink.
31	**One Hundred Pounds** Similar.	W	

Recorded printings of the £1 note

1 Mar 1925	15 May 1925	2 Jan 1926	1 Jul 1926

Cashier: William Lethbridge.
Accountant: Andrew McKissock.

29

The year 1927 saw the first major change in design for over 30 years. This change was limited to the £1 note, which is now issued in reduced size, the basic engraved plate printed in black and with a yellow and red lithographic overlay. The portrait is replaced by a vignette of Glasgow Cathedral and Edinburgh Castle by the Palace of Holyroodhouse. The lower vignettes are omitted. The back is printed in brown with yellow and red overlay and again features Princes Street and the Castle. One printed signature – that of the Cashier. Engraved by Waterlow & Sons Ltd. Numbered A/A to A/D.

1927

| 32 | **One Pound** | B | Black, red and yellow; back in brown |

Recorded printings

2 Nov 1927   2 Jul 1928   1 Nov 1929   2 Feb 1931

Cashiers: William Lethbridge; George Drever, 1931.

Four years later the contract for printing the £1 note passed to the Edinburgh firm of W. & A. K. Johnston. The notes are now printed by a deep-etch process and the design shows minor modifications consistent with the new method of printing. Other details are as before except, of course, for the change in the printers' imprint. Numbered A/E to A/G.

1931

| 33 | **One Pound** | B | Black, yellow and red; back in brown |

Printed by W. & A. K. Johnston.

Recorded printings:

2 Feb 1931   11 Nov 1932   11 Nov 1933

32

THE NATIONAL BANK OF SCOTLAND (contd.)

33

Cashier: George Drever.

Notes of £5 and upwards continued to be printed by Waterlow & Sons Ltd.

The Lord Lyon King of Arms took exception to the inclusion of the Royal Arms on the notes and these were replaced in 1934 by the Bank's own Arms. Other details remain unchanged. The £1 note continued to be printed by W. & A. K. Johnston and those of £5 and upwards by Waterlow & Sons Ltd.

1934

34	**One Pound**	B	Black, yellow and red; back in brown
	Bank Arms.		
35	**Five Pounds**	W	Blue, yellow and red
	Bank Arms.		

34

35

36 **Twenty Pounds**   w   Blue, yellow, red and pink
    Bank Arms.
37 **One Hundred Pounds**   w
    Similar.

"Specimens" of all denominations are known.

Recorded printings of the £1 note
                                                        12 Nov 1934
    1 Aug 1935   15 Apr 1936   2 Jan 1937   2 Feb 1937
    3 Aug 1937   7 Nov 1938   1 Jun 1939   20 Nov 1939
    31 Jul 1940   1 May 1941   23 Oct 1941   1 May 1942

Cashier: George Drever.

In 1943 the printed signature of the Cashier on the £1 note was replaced by
that of the General Manager and from 1 June 1953 the printers' imprint
reads W. & A. K. Johnston & G. W. Bacon Ltd. as a result of a merger
between these two firms. Considerable variations in colour of the overlay
exist in the many printings of this issue.

1943
38 **One Pound**   B   Black, yellow and red (shades);
                                       back in brown
        (*a*) Imprint W. & A. K. Johnston Ltd.
        (*b*) Imprint W. & A. K. Johnston & G. W. Bacon Ltd.

THE NATIONAL BANK OF SCOTLAND (contd.)

Recorded printings of the £1 note – W. & A. K. Johnston Ltd.

15 Mar 1943	15 May 1943	1 Nov 1944	15 Jun 1946
1 Mar 1947	1 Nov 1947	31 Jul 1948	30 Apr 1949
1 Dec 1949	1 Jun 1950	4 Jan 1951	5 Jul 1951
24 Jan 1952	1 Jul 1952	2 Jan 1953	

W. & A. K. Johnston & G. W. Bacon Ltd.

1 Jun 1953	11 Nov 1953	1 Jun 1954	1 Oct 1954
1 Mar 1955	3 Jan 1956	10 May 1956	1 Oct 1956
15 Jan 1957	28 Mar 1957	1 Jun 1957	1 Aug 1957
30 Nov 1957	1 Mar 1958	1 May 1958	10 May 1958
1 Jul 1958	1 Oct 1958	2 Feb 1959	1 May 1959
2 May 1959			

General Managers: J. T. Leggatt; J. A. Brown, from 1947; David Alexander, from 1956.

The design of the notes of £5 and upwards had remained basically unchanged since 1893 (apart from the substitution of the Bank's Arms for the Royal Arms) when an entirely new series was issued on 1 November 1957 from plates prepared by Waterlow & Sons Ltd. The design, which is in a reduced format (X) and modern in conception, features the Bank's Arms at left surmounted by a blank panel containing as a watermark a portrait of Sir Walter Scott and flanked by thistles. The Bank's title appears along the top of the note. The back has an illustration of the Forth railway bridge and is the forerunner of the series of Forth bridges later to be adopted as the main feature of the notes of National Commercial Bank of Scotland

39

Limited. A further innovation is the allocation of a different basic colour to each denomination printed from the engraved plates and including a multicolour lithographic overlay. Printed signatures of the General Manager and the Cashier. Engraved by Waterlow & Sons Ltd.

1957

39	**Five Pounds**	X	Green and multicolour
40	**Twenty Pounds**	X	Red and multicolour
41	**One Hundred Pounds**	X	Blue and multicolour

A small number of "specimen" notes of each denomination and bearing serial number A000-000 was prepared.

As the National Bank of Scotland Ltd. merged with the Commercial Bank of Scotland Ltd. in 1959 this attractive series had a very short life.

National Commercial Bank of Scotland Limited 1959–1969

This bank was the offspring of the marriage between the Commercial Bank of Scotland Ltd. and the National Bank of Scotland Ltd. which took place in 1959. During the ten years of its existence it was the largest of the Scottish banks, having a note circulation in excess of £45,000,000. In 1969 it combined with the Royal Bank of Scotland to form the National and Commercial Banking Group, the Scottish element of which operates under the title of the Royal Bank of Scotland *Limited*.

The first issue combined many of the features of the notes of the two constituent banks. All denominations were designed and engraved by Bradbury Wilkinson & Co. Ltd. and bear the signature of the General Manager. The £5 note was issued in reduced size on 3 January 1961.

1959

1 **One Pound**   B   Blue and multicolour
      The Forth railway bridge is the main feature and the back consists of an elaborate representation of the Arms of the new bank. The head of Caledonia appears as the watermark. One printing only – 16 September 1959.

2 **Five Pounds**   X   Green and multicolour
      The Arms of the Bank are featured in the lower portion of the note. The watermark consists of a portrait within a blank circular panel. The back illustrates the Forth railway bridge.
      One printing only – 16 September 1959.

NATIONAL COMMERCIAL BANK OF SCOTLAND LTD. (contd.)

1

3 **Twenty Pounds**   x   Red and multicolour
   Similar to the above.
4 **One Hundred Pounds**   x   Purple and multicolour
   Similar.

   "Specimen" notes of all denominations were prepared in small
   numbers for distribution within banking circles.

1961

5 **Five Pounds**   Y
   Similar to No. 2 but in reduced size. One printing only – 3 Jan
   1961.

On 1 November 1961 new £1 and (in 1963) new £5 notes were issued in the
now standardised colours of green and blue respectively, and in 1967 the
back of the £1 note was modified to include magnetic sorting marks. The
notes were designed and engraved by Bradbury Wilkinson & Co. Ltd.

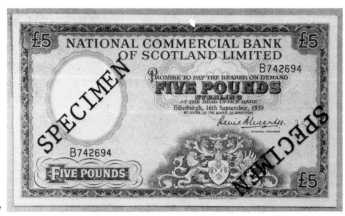

2

6

1961

6   **One Pound**   C   Green and multicolour
Similar in general design to the first £1 note but reduced in size.
Signature of General Manager.
(*a*) Without magnetic sorting marks.
(*b*) Modified to include sorting marks (1967).

Recorded printings

| 1 Nov 1961 | 1 Nov 1962 | 1 Aug 1963 | 1 Oct 1963 |
| 1 Oct 1964 | 4 Jan 1966 | | |

With magnetic sorting marks
4 Jan 1967   4 Jun 1967

1963

7   **Five Pounds**   Z   Blue and multicolour
Arms of the Bank on lower portion of the note. The back has a fine
engraving of Edinburgh Castle with the Royal Scottish Academy
and the National Gallery in the foreground.

As a result of public demand £10 notes were issued on 15 May 1966.

7

NATIONAL COMMERCIAL BANK OF SCOTLAND LTD. (contd.)

8

1966

8   **Ten Pounds**   Y   Brown and multicolour

The design is similar to that of the 1963 £5 note but the back illustrates the newly opened Tay road bridge with a panoramic view of Dundee in the background.

On 2 December 1968 new £1 notes in reduced size D were issued. These are dated 4 January 1968. The merger with the Royal Bank of Scotland had already been announced but as the new notes had been prepared beforehand it was decided to issue them.

1968

9   **One Pound**   D   Green and multicolour

Design similar to No. 6 but the illustration of the railway bridge has been redrawn to include the new road bridge in the background. Magnetic sorting marks.

All the above notes were designed and engraved by Bradbury Wilkinson & Co. Ltd.

"Specimens" overprinted and perforated were prepared in small numbers for distribution within banking circles.

9

The North British Bank   1844

Formed in 1844 by the Edinburgh board of directors of the Eastern Bank of Scotland after their decision to separate from the Dundee board and create an independent bank. Unfortunately before they could commence business under the new name the Bank Charter Act became law by which no new bank could acquire the right to issue notes. As the right of issue was at that time considered an essential part of banking they then applied to their Dundee colleagues to receive them back, but to this the Eastern Bank would not consent. They were therefore induced to accept the terms proposed by the City of Glasgow Bank for union with them. In effect, the North British Bank never got off the drawing board.

Plates for notes of the North British Bank had already been prepared and proofs of all denominations exist. A set of these is held in the collection of the Royal Bank of Scotland Limited.

1844

1   **One Pound**   A   *Proof.* Black: uniface
    Vignette of St. Andrew and Cross flanked by "One Pound" on either side in Gothic letters. Prepared for signatures of Accountant and Cashier. Engraved on steel by W. & A. K. Johnston.

2   **Five Pounds**   w   *Proof.* Black: uniface
    Of similar general design but the vignette is flanked on either side by the words "Five Pounds".

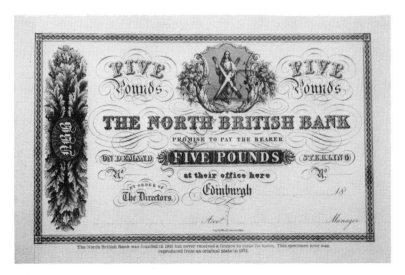

5

THE NORTH BRITISH BANK (contd.)

3　**Twenty Pounds**　　　　　w　　　*Proof.* Black: uniface
　　Similar, but vignette flanked on either side by "Twenty" and "Pounds" in ornamental characters.

4　**One Hundred Pounds**　　w　　　*Proof.* Black: uniface
　　Similar, but vignette flanked on either side by "100 Pounds".

In 1972 the original plate for the £5 note was discovered in Edinburgh and a limited number of impressions were taken from it for collectors. The impressions are on white paper and printed in black. They are overprinted "Specimen" and have a footnote in red "The North British Bank was founded in 1845 but never received a licence to issue its notes. This specimen note was reproduced from an original plate in 1972". The date in this footnote should have read "1844".

1972

5　**Five Pounds**　　　　　w
　　Reprint from the original plate.

The North of Scotland Banking Company 1836–1950
The North of Scotland Bank Limited
The North of Scotland & Town & County Bank Limited

The largest and most important of the Aberdeen-based banks. Founded in 1836 as the North of Scotland Banking Company it made rapid progress and opened a branch system which was to extend throughout Scotland. On registration in 1882 under the Companies Act the title North of Scotland Bank Ltd. was adopted. In 1907 the old rivalry between the North Bank and the Town & County Bank was ended by the merger of the banks under the title North of Scotland & Town & County Bank Ltd., reverting to North of Scotland Bank Ltd. in 1923. At this time the capital was purchased by the Midland Bank Ltd.; the Scottish bank, however, continued to operate on independent lines until 1950 when it merged with the other Scottish affiliate of the Midland Bank, the Clydesdale Bank Ltd., forming the Clydesdale & North of Scotland Bank Ltd.

　　The Authorised Circulation under the 1845 Act was £154,319.

　　Although the smallest of the twentieth century Scottish banks, apart from the Caledonian Bank, the North Bank displayed progressive trends in its note issue. It was the first to reduce the size of its notes and also the first to issue the various denominations in different colours.

I

The first issue consisted of denominations of £1, £5 and £20, all designed and engraved on steel plates by the Edinburgh firm of W. H. Lizars. All feature an engraving of Kings College, Aberdeen, which was to remain the principal motif for the next seventy years. The notes were dated and numbered by hand, and bore two signatures. All North Bank notes are payable to bearer.

1836

1 **One Pound**   A   Black: uniface
  Additional vignettes of two female statuesque figures at left and right. Signed on behalf of the Manager with one additional signature.
  An essay by Perkins Bacon & Co. is known. This is of similar general design, but all issued notes are from the Lizars plates.

2 **Five Pounds**   W   Black: uniface
  Additional vignettes representing Agriculture (left) and Commerce (right). Other details as above.

3 **Twenty Pounds**   W   Black: uniface
  Additional vignettes of Commerce seated (left) and Agriculture (right) Other details as above.

A proof (undated) of the £1 note is held by the Bank of Scotland in which "ONE" in green has been superimposed over the centre of the note. The issue of a note of this description cannot be confirmed.
  In 1862 the frame of the £5 note was modified to include "Established 1836 Incorporated 1862" and on 11 November 1865 a large panel comprising "FIVE" was superimposed on the legend panel in red.

THE NORTH OF SCOTLAND BANKING COMPANY (contd.)

1863

4 **Five Pounds**   W

As previous £5 note but with modified framework.

(a) Black: uniface.

(b) Black with panel "FIVE" in red (1865).

A proof of a £20 note held by the Royal Bank of Scotland Ltd. presents something of a mystery. It is identical to the Lizars note but bears the imprint of Gilmour & Dean of Glasgow. No notes bearing this imprint are known to have been issued.

The firm of W. H. Lizars was taken over by W. & A. K. Johnston in 1860 and notes following bear the imprint of the latter engravers. The plates were modified to include a small coat of Arms in the centre of the lower part of the note. "Established 1836 Incorporated 1862" is now also added to the framework of the £20 note. The backs now have a printed design in blue. The £1 note has been entirely re-designed.

1865

5 **One Pound**   A   Black and red; back printed in blue

Vignette of Kings College as before, but the two female allegorical figures are omitted. Signed on behalf of the Accountant and the Manager. Printed date and number.

6 **Five Pounds**   W   Black and red; back printed in
Similar to No. 4.   blue

7 **Twenty Pounds**   W   Black and red; back printed in
blue

Similar to the first £20 note but with added panel in red and inscription in the border.

8 **One Hundred Pounds**   W   Black and red; back printed in
blue

Design and details similar to £20 note.

In 1871 a £1 note in the same general design as that of the 1865 issue was printed from a plate prepared by Perkins Bacon & Co. It is printed in black with a panel in green containing "ONE" across the centre of the note. Printed number and date (29 September 1871).

1871

9 **One Pound**   A   Black and green: uniface
Engraved and printed by Perkins Bacon & Co.

All previously listed notes are inscribed "North of Scotland Banking Company". The following notes bear the inscription "North of Scotland Bank Limited", the existing plates being modified to accommodate the new title. Numbers and dates are printed. A £10 note was added to the series similar in general design but without allegorical figures at the left and right of the note.

1882

10   **One Pound**   A   Black and red; back printed in blue

   Inscribed North of Scotland Bank Limited. Other details as before.

11   **Five Pounds**   W
   Similar.

12   **Ten Pounds**   W
   New denomination. Black and red; back printed in blue.

13   **Twenty Pounds**   W
   Similar to £5 note.

14   **One Hundred Pounds**   W
   Similar.

   Proofs by W. H. Lizars and W. & A. K. Johnston exist in all denominations.

In 1908 the North of Scotland Bank Ltd. and the Town & County Bank Ltd. merged under the title of the North of Scotland & Town & County Bank Ltd. The Town & County Bank notes were re-issued bearing an overprint referring to the new name (*see* Town & County Bank).

THE NORTH OF SCOTLAND BANKING COMPANY (contd.)

On the merger the opportunity was taken to design an entirely new series of notes. These were printed from plates engraved by Bradbury Wilkinson & Co. Ltd. from a design by Sir George Reid, R.S.A., and feature as the main motif an engraving of the Marischal College, Aberdeen, at top centre and flanked by the figures of the value. A panel at the left contains the Arms of the Combined Bank, the County of Aberdeen and the City of Aberdeen. The watermark consists of the head of the Earl Marischal. The basic plate is printed in colours varying with the denomination and there is a lithographic overlay which also varies in colour. The back of the note features the Arms of the Bank. Signed on behalf of the General Manager and the Accountant, the early printings being hand-signed. The notes are printed on "granite" paper with the exception of some notes of the first printing of the £1 value, which are on plain paper.

1909

15 **One Pound**   A   Blue with sage green and yellow overlay.

   (*a*) Both signatures hand-signed. Plain paper.
   (*b*) Both signatures hand-signed. Granite paper.
   (*c*) Printed signature of General Manager and hand-signed on behalf of the Accountant.

16 **Five Pounds**   W   Blue with sage green and yellow overlay.

   (*a*) Both signatures hand-signed.
   (*b*) Signature of General Manager printed.

15

| 17 | **Twenty Pounds** | w | Purple with sage green and yellow overlay. |
| 18 | **One Hundred Pounds** | w | Brown with sage green and yellow overlay. |

Green appears as the dominant shade of all denominations.

Recorded printings of £1 value

1 Mar 1909	1 Mar 1910	1 Mar 1911	1 Mar 1912
1 Mar 1913	2 Mar 1914	1 Mar 1916	1 Mar 1918

All the above notes are inscribed "The North of Scotland & Town & County Bank Ltd.".

When the title of the Bank reverted to "North of Scotland Bank Ltd." in 1923 existing notes in circulation were overprinted with the shortened title, all other details remaining as before.

1923

19	**One Pound**	A

    Overprinted.
    (*a*) by rubber stamp.
    (*b*) With printed overprint.

19(a)

The overprint (at the top over existing Bank name) reads "Now the/North of Scotland Bank Limited".

THE NORTH OF SCOTLAND BANKING COMPANY *(contd.)*

20 **Five Pounds**   w
    Overprinted by rubber stamp.

21 **Twenty Pounds**   w
    Similar.

22 **One Hundred Pounds**   w
    Similar.

The plates were modified to incorporate the new title but other aspects of the design remain unchanged.

1923

23 **One Pound**   A   Brown with sage green and yellow overlay
    Inscribed North of Scotland Bank Ltd.

24 **Five Pounds**   w
    Similar.

25 **Twenty Pounds**   w   Purple with sage green and yellow overlay

26 **One Hundred Pounds**   w   Brown with sage green and yellow overlay.

The £1 note was issued in reduced size on 1 March 1924, the first Scottish note to conform to the size of the existing £1 Treasury note. The design is similar to that of the previous note but has a printed signature on behalf of the General Manager and is also initialled by hand on behalf of the Accountant.

24

27

1924
27 **One Pound**   B   Blue with sage green and yellow
                                     overlay
  Reduced size.

Recorded printings

  1 Mar 1924 1 Mar 1926

In 1928 the design of the £1 note was modified, the panels on either side of
the Marischal College containing the figure "1" instead of "£1". The
initials are now printed and are those of the Accountant and not on his
behalf.

1928
28 **One Pound**   B   Blue with sage green and yellow
                                     overlay
  Figures "1" instead of "£1".

Recorded printings

  1 Mar 1928 1 Mar 1932 1 Mar 1935

28

THE NORTH OF SCOTLAND BANKING COMPANY (contd.)

1935
29 **Five Pounds**   x   Blue with sage green and yellow
                                       overlay. As No. 24 but in reduced
                                       size.

Issue of a complete new series commenced in 1939. This was designed and
engraved by Thomas De La Rue & Co. Ltd., the main motif reverting to
Kings College. The design is common to all values but each denomination
is printed in a different colour from the basic plates. There are three Coats
of Arms, that of the Bank at top left, the County at top right and the City at
bottom right. The watermark features the head of Sir William Wallace
adapted from the profile of the Wallace Statue in Aberdeen. The £5, £20
and £100 notes, which are in a reduced size, were not issued until 1942.
The design on the back has the Bank Arms. These are very attractive notes;
a contemporary paragraph in the *Scottish Bankers' Magazine* reads "Not only
is the size very convenient but the design and colouring are beautiful.
Indeed one would wish to possess them for their artistic merit quite apart
from their intrinsic value". High praise from a technical publication!
    All notes have the printed signature of the General Manager.

1939
30 **One Pound**   B   Blue with sage green and yellow
                                     overlay.

1942
31 **Five Pounds**   x   Red with red overlay.

32 **Twenty Pounds**   x

33 **One Hundred Pounds**   x

30

31

Recorded printings of the £1 note

1 Jul	1938	(issued 1939)	1 Jul	1939	1 Jul	1940
1 Jul	1945	1 Jul 1946	1 Jul	1947	1 Jul	1948
1 Jul	1949					

The Paisley Banking Company   1783–1836

Established on 1 October 1783. Opened branches at Glasgow (1784), Irvine and Stranraer. On the expiry of the contract of co-partnership in November 1836 the business was transferred to the British Linen Company.

1783

  1   **Twenty Shillings**   A   Black: uniface
      Contemporary forgeries of this note were discovered in 1789.

  2   **Five Pounds**   W   Black: uniface
      Vignette of Abbot Schaw at top left. Vertical panel containing the arms of the Stewards, the Hamiltons and the Schaws. Dated and numbered by hand and signed by the Cashier and one other.

1820

  3   **One Pound**   A   Black: uniface
      Oval vignette with head of Abbot Schaw flanked by "One" and "Pound". Vertical panel at the left shows the shields of the Stewards, the Hamiltons and the Schaws. Dated and numbered by hand and signed by the Cashier and one other.
      Contemporary forgeries dated 1 February 1821 are known.

THE PAISLEY BANKING COMPANY (contd.)

3

4   **One Guinea**   A   Black: uniface

"One Guinea" flanked by two ovals. Panel on the left containing shields as in No. 3. Dated and numbered by hand and bearing two signatures. Printed revenue stamp on back.

Contemporary forgeries are known.

4

The Paisley Commercial Banking Company
1838–1844

Founded in 1838 with a capital of £200,000. Its life as an independent bank was short as it merged with the Western Bank of Scotland in 1844.

1838

1 **One Pound**   A   Black: uniface
   Portrait of Queen Victoria supported by two female figures and flanked by "One Pound" and "Paisley". Arms of Paisley in a central position at the bottom of the design. Printed revenue stamp on back. Dated and numbered by hand and signed by the Manager and the Accountant. Engraved on steel by Joseph Swan, Glasgow.

2 **Five Pounds**   W   Black: uniface
   Portrait of Queen Victoria with Paisley Abbey in the background. Vignettes representing Industry and Commerce at left and right respectively. Arms of Paisley in a small panel at the bottom. Dated and numbered by hand and signed by the Manager and the Accountant. Engraved on steel by W. H. Lizars.

3 **Twenty Pounds**   W   Black: uniface
   Portrait as on £5 note but with title of the Bank in curved lettering above. Other details similar.

   Proofs of the £5 and £20 notes exist.

The Paisley Union Banking Company   1788–1838
The Paisley Union Bank

Established at Paisley on 9 September 1788 with a capital of £10,000. It opened branches as far apart as Oban and Berwick and also invaded England by opening at Carlisle and Penrith. In 1811 the branch at Glasgow was the scene of the most famous of Scottish bank robberies. The circulation in 1789 amounted to £59,750 rising to £108,332 in 1836. It merged in the Glasgow Union Bank in 1838.

1788

1 **One Guinea**   A   Black: uniface
   Arms within a wreath flanked by "One Guinea" and "Paisley". Dated and numbered by hand and signed by the Cashier and one other. Watermarked "The Union Bank Paisley". Engraved by Kirkwood & Son.

THE PAISLEY UNION BANKING COMPANY (contd.)

2   **Five Pounds**   w   Black: uniface
Similar general design to that of the £1 note but the vignette is
flanked by "Five Pounds" and "Paisley". Dated and numbered by
hand and signed by the Cashier and one other. Watermarked "The
Union Bank Paisley". Engraved by Kirkwood & Son.

1822

3   **One Guinea**   A   Black: uniface
Arms in an oval wreath of thistles and roses at top centre flanked
by "One Guinea" and "£1,1– Paisley". Dated and numbered by
hand. Printed revenue stamp on back. Signed by the Cashier and
one other and designed and engraved by Kirkwood & Son.

3

1827

4   **One Pound**   A   Black: uniface
Similar vignette to that on the 1 guinea note but placed at top left.
"One Pound" to the right. Dated and numbered by hand. Printed
revenue stamp on back. Designed and engraved by Kirkwood &
Son. Signed by the Cashier and one other.
Contemporary forgery known dated 18 June 1827.

The Perth Banking Company   1787–1857
The Perth Banking Company 1787–1808
The Perth Banking Company 1808–1829
The Perth Banking Company 1829–1857

Opened at Perth on 7 May 1787 as a joint stock company formed to take over the business of the Perth United Company and with an original capital of £34,000. In accordance with practice the contract of the company was for a period of 21 years after which it went into voluntary liquidation, the capital being repaid. A new company with the same name was immediately formed to take over the business and the same procedure was adopted in 1829. Although therefore we are dealing with three separate companies it is appropriate and convenient to treat them as one, as each company retired the notes of its predecessor and issued new notes of a similar design. The business of the bank, or rather the succession of banks, flourished. The amount of notes in circulation in 1808 totalled £83,200 but this figure declined in later years, the Authorised Circulation under the 1845 Act being £38,656. In 1857 it was agreed to merge in the Union Bank of Scotland and from 1858 the business at Perth and the branches was carried on under the name of the Union Bank.

1787
  1   **One Guinea**   A   Black: uniface
       Arms of Perth. Designed to resemble the notes of the Perth United Company.
  2   **Five Pounds**   W   Black: uniface
       Similar.

1798
  3   **Five Shillings** 125 × 95 mm   Black: uniface
       Circular vignette of the Arms of Perth at top left. "Five Shillings" at the right. Printed date 1 January 1798 but numbered by hand. Payable to Walter Miller and signed by the Cashier and one other. Designed and engraved by Kirkwood & Son.

1806
  4   **Twenty Shillings**   A   Black: uniface
       Oval vignette of Arms to the left. "Twenty Shillings" at the right. Dated and numbered by hand and with an embossed revenue stamp. Watermarked "Perth Bank" in an oval. Signed by the Cashier and one other. Designed by G. Paton and engraved by Kirkwood & Son.

THE PERTH BANKING COMPANY (contd.)

Contemporary forgery known dated 1 September 1812 on which the engravers' imprint reads "Perth Banking Company" instead of Kirkwood & Son. Without any watermark.

1808

5   **One Guinea**   A   Black: uniface
Arms in a central position flanked by "One Guinea" and "Perth". Dated and numbered by hand. Embossed revenue stamp. Watermarked "Perth Bank" in an oval. Designed and engraved by Kirkwood & Son.

6   **Five Pounds**   W   Black: uniface
Similar.

7   **Ten Pounds**   W
Similar.

8   **Twenty Pounds**   W
Similar.

1820

9   **Twenty Shillings**   A   Black, blue and red: uniface
Circular vignette of Arms in blue at left with "Twenty Shillings" in Gothic script at the right. Vertical panel at left in red. Dated and numbered by hand. Embossed revenue stamp. Watermarked "Perth Bank" in an oval. Signed by the Cashier and one other. Engraved by Kirkwood & Son.

In 1829 the notes of the old company were overprinted by means of a stamp.

1833

10 **Twenty Shillings**   A   Black: uniface
Similar to the 1820 issue but now printed entirely in black. Printed revenue stamp on back. Other details as previous issue.

Contemporary forgeries dated 1 September 1835 and 6 November 1836 are without engravers' imprint or watermark.

In 1850, no doubt because of the incidence of forgeries in the previous design, new plates with a design "of a character more difficult of imitation" were prepared. These were steel plates designed and engraved by W. H. Lizars from which were printed very attractive notes indeed. The printing of all denominations was in black but the backs were engraved with a representation of the Perth Arms in blue. The notes were signed by the Cashier and one other, dated by hand but with printed numbers. They had no watermark.

11

1850

11   **One Pound**   A   Black; back printed in blue
     Arms of Perth at top centre flanked on each side by "One". Full
     length figures of Queen Victoria and Prince Albert at left and right
     respectively.

12   **Five Pounds**   W   Black; back printed in blue
     Arms at top centre flanked on each side by "Five". Engravings of
     Queen Victoria and Prince Albert on horseback at left and right.

13   **Twenty Pounds**   W   Black; back printed in blue
     Arms flanked by "Twenty" and "Pounds". Half length portraits of
     Queen Victoria and Prince Albert at left and right.
     Proofs of all three values exist.

13

THE PERTH BANKING COMPANY (contd.)

In 1856 the Bank was incorporated under the Companies Act and the plates were modified to include "Pursuant to Act of Parliament" at the top and "16–17 Vict. Cap.65" at the foot. Other details were unchanged.

1856

14   **One Pound**   A   Black: back printed in blue
         "Pursuant to Act of Parliament".

15   **Five Pounds**   W
         Similar.

16   **Twenty Pounds**   W
         Similar.

On the merger with the Union Bank of Scotland existing Perth notes continued to be issued for a short period overprinted "Union Bank of Scotland". The overprint is at top or bottom of the note clear of the edge of the design.

1858

17   **One Pound**   A
         Previous issue overprinted "Union Bank of Scotland".
         (*a*) Overprinted at the top in blue.
         (*b*) Overprinted at top and bottom in red.

18   **Five Pounds**   W
         Overprinted at the top in black.

The Perth Union Bank   1810–1836

Established at Perth in 1810 and with three branches, this bank had an uneventful career and finally amalgamated with the National Bank of Scotland in 1836.

1810

1   **One Pound**   A   Black: uniface
        Reclining female figure with bridge over the River Tay in the background, and flanked by "20 Shillings" and "£1 Perth". Dated and numbered by hand and signed by the Cashier and the Accountant. Engraved on a copper plate by Kirkwood & Son.
        Contemporary forgeries are known dated 1 April 1815 and 1 June 1815.

The Perth United Company   1766–1787

This bank was formed in 1766 to amalgamate the businesses of six small companies carrying on banking business in Perth. These were:

THE PERTH BANKING COMPANY John Stewart & Company	1763	1 Their notes had a vignette of the City Arms.
THE TANNERIE BANKING COMPANY Stewart Buchanan & Company	1764	2 Notes had a vignette of an oak tree.
THE BANKING COMPANY Wedderspoon & Company	1764	3 Notes had a vignette of a crowned thistle.
THE BANKING COMPANY McKeith Rintoul & Company	1764	4 Notes had a portrait of the King.
THE CRAIGIE BANKING COMPANY John Ramsay & Company	1764	5 Notes had a vignette of a sheaf of grain.
THE BANKING COMPANY John Bruce	1764	6 Notes had a vignette of the Bruce crest and motto.

None of these notes has been seen by the author and there is no record of the actual denominations. In *The History of the Union Bank of Scotland* it is stated that they adopted the Option Clause and were issued for trivial sums. The Act of 1765 prohibited the issue of notes for less than £1 and no doubt provided the reason for their agreement to combine in the Perth United Company. The six banks traded in a very small way and their notes could only have been in circulation for little over a year.

The United Company flourished and had a note circulation of £83,200 in 1777. In accordance with the custom of the time it went into voluntary liquidation at the end of the twenty-one years agreed to in the contract of co-partnery. It was succeeded by the Perth Banking Company which took over the business and retired the notes.

1766

7 **One Guinea**   A   Black: uniface
   Vignette of the Arms of Perth. Dated and numbered by hand. Two signatures.

8 **Five Pounds**   W   Black: uniface
   Similar to the 1 guinea note.

JOHN RAMSAY & COMPANY
See the Perth United Company.

Ramsays Bonars & Company   1738–1837
Mansfield Hunter & Company
Mansfield Ramsay & Company

This private bank had a long life. The firm dates back to 1738 but it is un-likely that any form of banking business was included among its mercantile activities in the early years. It voluntarily retired from business in 1837.

IN NAME OF MANSFIELD HUNTER & COMPANY

1761

1   Five Shillings   A   Black: uniface

IN NAME OF RAMSAYS BONARS & COMPANY

1807

2   Ten Pounds   W   Black: uniface
    Vignette of the Royal Exchange, Edinburgh, surmounted by "Edinburgh" and flanked on each side by "Ten". Dated and numbered by hand. Two signatures. Engraved on steel by W. H. Lizars.

3   Twenty Pounds   W   Black: uniface
    Similar vignette surmounted by "Royal Exchange" and flanked by "Twenty" and "Pounds". Dated and numbered by hand. Two signatures. Engraved on steel by W. H. Lizars.

Proofs of both denominations exist.

These are the earliest recorded steel-engraved banknotes by W. H. Lizars.

The Renfrewshire Banking Company   1802–1842
Sir William Napier & Company

Founded at Greenock in 1802, it had five branches in all. It was se-questrated on 1 April 1842 with debts totalling £226,545 and paid about 9s. in the £ as a dividend to the creditors. Holders of notes dated prior to 1840 were paid in full by a former partner.

3

1802

1 **One Guinea**   A   Black: uniface

1821

2 **One Guinea**   A   Black: uniface
Vignette of reclining lion with shield. Dated and numbered by hand and signed by the Manager, the Cashier and the Accountant. Designed by G. Paton and engraved by Kirkwood & Son.

1830

3 **One Pound**   A   Black: uniface
Central vignette of female figure flanked by two ovals containing the figure "1" on the left and the note number on the right. Dated and numbered by hand and bearing the signatures of the Manager, the Cashier and the Accountant. Engraved on steel by Perkins & Heath. Printed revenue stamp on the back.

4 **Five Pounds**   W   Black: uniface
Central vignette of Arms flanked by "Five Pounds" and "Greenock". Dated and numbered by hand. Three signatures. Designed by G. Paton. Engraved by Kirkwood & Son.

Most £1 notes seen have an oval stamp marked "Ranked", signifying that they had been submitted to the liquidator in application for dividend.

R. Robertson Jr. & Company   1765

Established in Perth, this was probably a mercantile firm not engaged in banking as such. The note described is in the collection of the National Museum of Antiquities in Edinburgh and no others have been seen.

1765
1   **Five Shillings**   110 × 75 mm   Black: uniface
    Small oval vignette containing portrait and flanked by "£3 Scots" and "Perth". Inscribed ". . . Five Shillings Sterling value received in goods". Dated and numbered by hand and signed in the firm's name.

The Royal Bank of Scotland   1727–1969

The history of a bank of such long standing as the Royal Bank of Scotland must of necessity reflect something of the history of the country itself, and indeed its origin had a close connection with the Treaty of Union with England. One provision of this Treaty set aside the sum of £398,065 10s., known as the Equivalent, to enable Scotland to assume a share in certain fiscal commitments of the newly established United Kingdom. In 1719 an Act was passed settling the Equivalent at the figure at which it then stood, creating for the outstanding creditors a company known as the Equivalent Company with a capital of £24,855. The proprietors of the new company soon began to search for a profitable utilisation of their capital, resulting in a Charter being granted on 31 May 1727 enabling those who so elected to subscribe their capital to "One Body Politic and Corporate of themselves in Deed and Name, by name of The Royal Bank of Scotland".

The consternation shown by the Bank of Scotland at these events is understandable and so the "Battle of the Banks" commenced. The "Royal", however, was soundly established and soon earned for itself a reputation for reliability, handling much of the Government's Scottish business. In 1728 it introduced the Cash Credit system which was to become a feature of Scottish banking and which in fact can claim to be the forerunner of the now familiar overdraft. The system contributed much to the economic development of Scotland, a country which had for long suffered from lack of capital.

The Royal Bank did not pursue the opening of branches with quite the same vigour as did some of its competitors and it was not until well into the nineteenth century before it expanded in this direction. In 1864 it absorbed the Dundee Banking Company but it was not until fairly recent times that further expansion took place. At a time when three major English banks had acquired the capital of Scottish institutions the "Royal" embarked on the course of purchasing English banks! Drummonds Bank was acquired in 1924, Williams Deacons Bank and Glyn Mills & Co. in 1930 and 1939. Nothing daunted it also took over the Western Branch of the Bank of England in 1930.

As with other institutions in this book, the history of a bank such as the Royal can only be briefly referred to here and the attention of readers is directed to the Bibliography. The bank's long career came to an end in 1969 when a merger was arranged with National Commercial Bank of Scotland Limited, at that time the largest of the Scottish Banks, the child of that marriage being the present Royal Bank of Scotland Limited.

The Authorised Circulation under the 1845 Act was £183,000 but the actual circulation exceeded £22 million.

The first issue consisted of the denominations 20s., £10, £20, £50 and £100. All were printed in black and are uniface. A portrait of George II appears in an oval vignette at top left. The notes were designed by David Beatt, Writing Master, and engraved on copper plates by Joseph Cave, Engraver at the Mint. As a security measure all notes were embossed with the Bank's seal. They are made payable to David Campbell, the first Secretary of the Bank, and are signed by Thomas Thomson, Accountant, and Allan Whitefoord, Cashier. Printing was done on the Bank premises. The notes are dated 8 December 1727.

1727
1 Twenty Shillings   A   Black: uniface
2 Ten Pounds   A
   Similar.
3 Twenty Pounds   A
   Similar.
4 Fifty Pounds   A
   Similar. The only issue of this denomination.
5 One Hundred Pounds   A
   Similar.

Two specimens of the 20s. note are in the collection of the Royal Bank of Scotland Ltd. but it is doubtful if any of the others have survived.

A second 20s. note was issued on 6 April 1742. This again has the portrait of George II but differs from the first by being more ornate and is additionally inscribed "Twelve Pounds Scots". It is payable to John Graham and signed by the Accountant and the Cashier. Embossed with the Bank's seal. Engraved on a copper plate by Richard Cooper.

THE ROYAL BANK OF SCOTLAND (contd.)

1742
  6 **Twenty Shillings**   A   Black: uniface

The third 20s. note was issued on 9 February 1750. This has a portrait of the King in profile and is printed from a copper plate, giving excellent quality for the period. It is payable to the Secretary and signed by the Accountant and the Cashier. It is additionally inscribed "£12 Scots" at the top. Although numbered by hand it has the date printed. No further 20s. or £1 notes were printed until 1792, with the exception of those bearing the Option Clause in 1762.

1750
  7 **Twenty Shillings**   A   Black: uniface

   It is assumed that notes of £10 and over of the original series continued to be issued until this time but it has not been possible to confirm this from the records.

The first Scottish 1 guinea note was issued by the Royal Bank in 1758. This was printed from a copper plate engraved by Robert Cooper of London and again has the King's portrait. It is payable to the Secretary and signed by the Accountant and the Cashier. The text includes the words "Pursuant to Act of Parliament and Letters Patent under the Great Seal" in order to underline the standing of the Bank.

1758
  8 **One Guinea**   A   Black: uniface

On 5 April 1762 notes were issued containing the Option Clause which on the £1 note reads "One Pound sterling on demand or in the Option of the Directors One Pound Sixpence sterling at the End of Six Months after the Day of the Demand". The notes bear a semi-facing portrait of George III in a small vignette at top left. They are numbered by hand but have printed dates. Signed by the Accountant and the Cashier, they are embossed with the Bank's seal.

1762
  9 **One Pound**   A   Black: uniface
       With Option Clause.
 10 **Ten Pounds**   A
       Similar.
 11 **Twenty Pounds**   A
       Similar.
 12 **One Hundred Pounds**   A
       Similar.

13

A second type of 1 guinea note was issued on 1 September 1777. This is of rather historic importance being the first British note to be printed in three colours. The main feature is the head of George III in the form of the obverse of the gold guinea piece. This is printed in red and in consequence the note is referred to in the Bank records as the "Red Head Issue". A small rectangular panel containing the value is printed in blue at the top right of the note. The remainder of the note is printed in black from a copper plate. Numbered by hand but with a printed date. Signed by the Accountant and the Cashier and embossed with the Bank's seal.

1777

13	One Guinea	A	Black, red and blue: uniface
	The "Red Head Issue".		

Notes of the larger denominations were issued in 1785. These have the portrait of George III but other details of the design are not known.

1785

14	Five Pounds	W	Black: uniface
15	Ten Pounds	W	
	Similar.		
16	Twenty Pounds	W	
	Similar.		
17	One Hundred Pounds	W	
	Similar.		

THE ROYAL BANK OF SCOTLAND (contd.)

Twenty Shilling Notes were again issued on 9 February 1792. These have the King's portrait in profile and although printed in black have the serial number in red at the left of the note. Numbered by hand and with a printed date. Signed by the Accountant and the Cashier and embossed with the Bank's seal and additionally with the revenue stamp.

1792

18   Twenty Shillings   A   Black, with serial number in red: uniface

Because of the shortage of specie, notes of 5s. were issued on 3 April 1797 as a temporary measure. These were printed in black from a copper plate engraved by Robert Kirkwood and have a panel at the left composed of thistles and a crown. Payable to James Innes, they are numbered by hand but have a printed date. Signed on behalf of the Accountant and the Cashier. The first Royal Bank notes to have an engravers' or printers' imprint.

1797

19   Five Shillings   A   Black: uniface

A third 1 guinea note was issued on 2 December 1799 with the coinage head of George III as a central motif flanked by "One" and "Guinea" in Gothic script. Numbered by hand in red ink but with printed date. Payable to James Innes and signed on behalf of the Accountant and the Cashier. Printed from a copper plate engraved by Kirkwood & Son. Embossed revenue stamp.

18

1799
20   **One Guinea**   A   Black: uniface

A new £1 note was issued on 25 March 1801. This was printed from a
copper plate engraved by Kirkwood & Son and features as a central motif
the Royal Regalia. It is referred to in the Bank records as the "Regalia
Issue". Payable to James Innes, it has a printed date but is numbered by
hand. Signed on behalf of the Accountant and the Cashier. Embossed
revenue stamp.

1801
21   **One Pound**   A   Black: uniface
        The "Regalia Issue".

The design of the Regalia Issue was altered around 1807 to feature the
Crown only, surmounted by the words "One Pound", although "Twenty
Shillings" continues to be the value expressed in the legend. Printed from a
copper plate engraved by Kirkwood & Son it is both dated and numbered
by hand. Payable first to George Mitchell, Secretary, and later to his
successor Andrew Bogle and signed on behalf of the Accountant and the
Cashier. Embossed revenue stamp until 1808 when the Royal Bank was
permitted to compound the duty.

1807
22   **Twenty Shillings**   A   Black: uniface
        (a) Payable to George Mitchell.
        (b) Payable to Andrew Bogle.
        Embossed revenue stamp until 1808.
     Contemporary forgeries exist.

A fourth 1 guinea note made its appearance in 1813, again with the coinage
head of George III. This is flanked by the words "Edinburgh" and "One
Guinea". Printed from a copper plate engraved by Kirkwood & Son and
payable to Andrew Bogle. Dated and numbered by hand and signed on
behalf of the Accountant and the Cashier.

1813
23   **One Guinea**   A   Black: uniface

There is now a complete departure from the previous designs. In 1826 the
famous Edinburgh engraver W. H. Lizars produced from a steel plate a
new 20s. note which was technically well in advance of its time. The royal
portrait is again the central feature but it is contained within a circular
frame of intricate engine work and flanked on each side by circular and
oval panels of the same type of engraving. Two oval panels, again of similar

THE ROYAL BANK OF SCOTLAND (contd.)

geometric engraving, are at left (containing "Bearer") and right (containing "Sterling"). It is the first Royal Bank note to have a printed back consisting of more elaborate geometric engraving. The whole design is reminiscent of the Perkins Bacon steel engraving of the next decade. Numbered and dated by hand and signed on behalf of the Accountant and Cashier.

1826

24 Twenty Shillings   A   Black; printed back. Engraved
                                     on steel
          Dates of issue: 4 Nov 1826 5 Apr 1827 6 May 1831 9 May 1832

The last type of 1 guinea note made its appearance on 4 November 1826. This had a central motif of a reclining female figure (Britannia?) with a lion crouched at her side. There are a number of geometric panels similar to those in the 1826-type 20s. note. Payable to Andrew Bogle and signed on behalf of the Accountant and the Cashier. Dated and numbered by hand.

1826

25 **One Guinea**   A   Black; the back is printed with an
                                     elaborate panel

The design of the notes of £5 and upwards current at this time consists of a portrait of George II in an oval at the left of the note surmounted by the value L5, L10, etc. (note the absence of the £ symbol). This design is relatively simple and indeed has the appearance of a note of the eighteenth century. It is possible that the plates may have been in use for a considerable time but the date of their introduction cannot be confirmed. The year 1830 is selected but the appropriate date is probably earlier. They are dated and numbered by hand and signed by the Accountant and the Cashier. The name of the Secretary to whom they are made payable is inserted by hand.

1830

26 **Five Pounds**   W   Black: uniface

27 **Ten Pounds**   W
        Similar.

28 **Twenty Pounds**   W
        Similar.

29 **One Hundred Pounds** W
        Similar.

          Proofs of the £5 and £10 notes exist.

On 9 November 1832 20s. notes were issued from a steel plate engraved by W. H. Lizars. The design, which was to continue in its basic form for over a century, consists of the portrait of George I flanked by the unicorn and the lion of the Royal Arms. The seated figure of Britannia and the standing figure representing Plenty and holding a cornucopia are on the left and right of the note. Dated and numbered by hand they are signed on behalf of the Accountant and the Cashier. (*Pr.* Accot. and *Pr.* Cashier). Payable to Robert Sym Wilson, Secretary and, from 1845, to his successor James Wright.

1832
30 **Twenty Shillings**   A   Black: uniface
    (*a*) Payable to Robert Sym Wilson.
    (*b*) Payable to James Wright (1845).

The first modification was in 1853, the note now being inscribed "One Pound" instead of "Twenty Shillings". Other details as before. Payable to James Wright.

1853
31 **One Pound**   A   Black: uniface

In 1854 the plates of the high-denomination notes were altered to include "Pursuant to Act of Parliament" at the top of the note. Although they continue to be dated by hand they now have printed numbers. The Secretary's name is still inserted by hand and the notes are signed *on behalf of* the Accountant and the Cashier.

1854
32 **Five Pounds**   w   Black: uniface
    "Pursuant to Act of Parliament".

33 **Ten Pounds**   w
    Similar.

34 **Twenty Pounds**   w
    Similar.

35 **One Hundred Pounds**   w
    Similar.

Specimens overprinted "Cancelled" exist.

In order to provide greater security the "Lizars" £1 note was printed in bright blue in 1860. Large ornate letters R B S are placed on the centre of the note. Both date and number are now printed and the note is signed as

THE ROYAL BANK OF SCOTLAND (contd.)

32

before but with the designations changed to *P.Accot.* and *P.Cashier.*
Payable to James Wright.

1860

| 36 | **One Pound** | A | Blue and red: uniface |

New designs for the "large" notes were prepared in 1861 by W. & A. K.
Johnston. These incorporate the Royal Arms of the current £1 notes
flanked by words and figures of the value, the words being printed in red.
A lithographic overlay in red is superimposed on the legend panel. The
number and the Secretary's name are printed but the notes continue to be
dated by hand. Signed on behalf of the Accountant and the Cashier. Embossed with the Bank's seal.

All current and future notes are watermarked "Royal Bank of Scotland".

1861

37	**Five Pounds**	w	Black and red: uniface
38	**Ten Pounds**	w	
	Similar.		
39	**Twenty Pounds**	w	
	Similar.		
40	**One Hundred Pounds**	w	
	Similar.		

"Pursuant to Act of Parliament" was added to the top of the £1 note in 1865. The printers' imprint is now W. & A. K. Johnston, this firm having taken over W. H. Lizars in 1860 on the death of Mr. Lizars the previous year. Payable to James Wright. Other details as before.

1865
41 **One Pound** A Blue and red: uniface
    Imprint W. & A. K. Johnston.

The designs of the "large" notes were modified in 1877 by the introduction of a new vertical panel at the left of the note. The Bank's title is now in Gothic letters. Printing from the engraved plate is now in blue while the lithographic overlay remains in red. Signatures of the Accountant and the Cashier. Other details as before.

1877
42 **Five Pounds** W Blue and red: uniface
    (a) Imprint W. & A. K. Johnston.
    (b) Imprint W. & A. K. Johnston Limited.
    (c) Imprint W. & A. K. Johnston & G. W. Bacon Ltd.
    (d) Blue, red and yellow (1940).

43 **Ten Pounds** W Blue and red: uniface
    (a) Plate C 1877–1918. The network overlay is almost invisible.
    (b) Plate D 1918–1969. Blue and red with yellow overlay. The blue is much darker than Plate C.

44 **Twenty Pounds** W Blue and red: uniface
    (a) Plate C 1877–1913. Very pale overlay.
    (b) Plate D 1914–1947. Blue and red with yellow overlay. Imprint W. & A. K. Johnston Ltd.
    (c) Plate E, similar, 1947–1952.
    (d) Plates F, G and H 1952–1969. Imprint W. & A. K. Johnston & G. W. Bacon Ltd. Both signatures printed.

45 **One Hundred Pounds** W Blue and red: uniface
    (a) Plate C 1877–1918. Very pale overlay.
    (b) Plates D and E 1918–1960. Yellow overlay.
    (c) Plate F and G 1960–1969. Imprint W. & A. K. Johnston & G. W. Bacon Ltd. Both signatures printed.

The custom of making notes payable to an officer of the Bank was discontinued in 1875 and they are now made payable to bearer. The plate for the £1 note was suitably modified. The signature of the Accountant is now printed but notes continue to be signed by hand on behalf of the Cashier.

THE ROYAL BANK OF SCOTLAND (contd.)

1875

46 **One Pound**   A   Blue and red

There is a lithographic network over the whole area of the note that is practically invisible. Printed signature of Accountant.

(a) W. Turnbull 1875–1878.

(b) F. A. Mackay 1878–1887.

(c) W. Templeton 1887–1908.

(d) D. S. Lunan 1908–1920.

(e) D. Speed 1920–1927. The overlay on this issue shows pale yellow. Serial letter in red.

Recorded printings:

2 Jan 1903	5 May 1908	2 Jan 1913	16 Jul 1914
30 Dec 1914	1 Jul 1915	24 Dec 1915	25 Jul 1916
10 Mar 1917	1 Sep 1917	2 Feb 1918	29 Jun 1918
20 Feb 1919	29 Jun 1919	24 Mar 1920	14 May 1920
24 Mar 1921	29 Jun 1921	20 Feb 1922	28 Aug 1922
24 Mar 1923	7 Jul 1923	20 Feb 1924	29 Oct 1924
14 May 1925	25 Nov 1925	14 May 1926	

Truly a remarkable note to have remained in issue for so long with only minor modification and one which offers wonderful scope for specialisation.

Printers' proofs in blue and in black exist covering the 1850–1875 period.

An essay by W. & A. K. Johnston exists with a similar basic design but printed in multicolour with an illustration of the Bank's Head Office on the back also printed in several colours. This is dated 7 July 1913.

A finely engraved essay by Bradbury Wilkinson & Co. Ltd. is dated 1914.

Further essays exist dated 1921 submitted by Waterlow & Sons Ltd.

In common with the other Scottish banks the £1 note was issued in reduced size in 1927. The basic features of the "Lizars" note are retained but with a printed back containing illustrations of the Head Office and the principal office in Glasgow in circular panels. This note is printed by a deep-etch off-set process with a lithographic overlay in reddish-brown. It has a printed signature of David Speed, the Accountant, and is additionally hand-signed on behalf of the Cashier. This is the last Scottish £1 note to have a manuscript signature.

1927

47 **One Pound**   B   Blue and red-brown with an
                                                    almost invisible pale yellow
                                                    overlay

Recorded printings:

2 Feb 1927	30 Nov 1927	15 Oct 1928	14 Oct 1929
30 May 1930	16 Oct 1930	11 Nov 1931	31 Oct 1932
31 Oct 1933	31 Oct 1934	31 Oct 1935	

From 1936 the £1 note has only one signature, that of the Chief Accountant, which is printed. The overlay ranges from a very pale shade in the early printings to yellow from 1944.

1936

48   **One Pound**   B   Blue and red-brown
      Signature of Chief Accountant.
      (a) David Speed 1936. Printers' imprint W. & A. K. Johnston Ltd.
      (b) Blue, red-brown and yellow. Thomas Brown 1944.
      (c) J. D. C. Dick 1953.
      (d) Printers' imprint: W. & A. K. Johnston & G. W. Bacon Ltd. (1
      April 1953).

On 1 April 1955 the printed signature was changed to that of the General Manager. The yellow overlay is now in a much deeper shade. Other details as before.

1955

49   **One Pound**   B   Blue, red-brown and yellow
      Signature of General Manager.

Recorded printings of the £1 note (Nos. 48 and 49)

2 Jan 1937	30 Jan 1937	3 Jan 1938	1 Dec 1938
1 Sep 1939	1 Sep 1940	1 Sep 1941	1 Jul 1942
1 Mar 1943	6 Jan 1944	1 Dec 1944	24 Jan 1946
25 Apr 1946	6 Jan 1947	1 Oct 1947	11 Oct 1948
1 Oct 1949	2 Jan 1951	16 Jul 1951	1 Feb 1952
2 Jun 1952	1 Nov 1952	1 Apr 1953	1 Aug 1953
1 Dec 1953	1 Apr 1954	1 Jul 1954	1 Oct 1954
3 Jan 1955	1 Apr 1955	1 Aug 1955	1 Nov 1955
1 Feb 1956	1 Jun 1956	1 Sep 1956	1 Nov 1956
1 Mar 1957	1 Jul 1957	1 Oct 1957	1 Feb 1958
1 Apr 1958	1 Nov 1958	2 Feb 1959	1 Apr 1959
1 Sep 1959	2 Nov 1959	1 Mar 1960	1 Jun 1960
1 Sep 1960	1 Nov 1960	1 Feb 1961	1 Apr 1961
11 Apr 1961	2 Oct 1961	1 Jun 1961	2 Jan 1962
1 Mar 1962	1 May 1962	1 Aug 1962	1 Oct 1962
2 Jan 1963	2 Apr 1963	1 Jun 1963	2 Sep 1963
2 Dec 1963	2 Mar 1964	1 May 1964	1 Jul 1964

THE ROYAL BANK OF SCOTLAND (contd.)

Three years earlier, the £5 note was issued in reduced size on 2 January 1952. Both signatures are now printed and are those of the Cashier & General Manager and of the Chief Accountant. In 1954 there were three signatures, two being those of the joint Cashiers & General Managers and the third of the Chief Accountant. The design and other details are similar to the previous issue.

1952

50   **Five Pounds**   X   Blue, red and yellow: uniface
    (a) Two signatures. Printers' imprint W. & A. K. Johnston Ltd.
    (b) Three signatures (1954). Printers' imprint: W. & A. K. Johnston & G. W. Bacon Ltd.

The £1 note was issued on 1 December 1964 in size C and the £5 note in size Z. The designs are similar to the previous issues.

1964

51   **One Pound**   C   Blue, red-brown and yellow
    Printed signature of General Manager.
    (a) W. R. Ballantyne 1964.
    (b) G. P. Robertson 1965.

Recorded printings

1 Aug 1964	1 Nov 1964	1 Dec 1964	1 Mar 1965
1 Apr 1965	1 May 1965	1 Jun 1965	2 Aug 1965
1 Oct 1965	1 Dec 1965	2 Jan 1966	1 Feb 1966
1 Mar 1966	1 Apr 1966	1 Jun 1966	1 Jul 1966
1 Oct 1966	3 Jan 1967	1 Mar 1967	1 May 1967
1 Jun 1967	1 Jul 1967	1 Sep 1967	1 Nov 1967

52

52   **Five Pounds**   z   Blue red and yellow: uniface
     Printed signatures of the General Manager and the Chief Accoun-
     tant.

The £5 notes were subjected to a dangerous forgery, aided no doubt
by the simplicity of the design.

In 1966 the first change in basic design for over 130 years took place, the
opportunity being taken to incorporate the best elements of security printing. The new notes were designed and engraved by Bradbury Wilkinson &
Co. Ltd. and are very attractive indeed, the £5 note being considered by
some to be the finest of modern Scottish issues. This note features a large
portrait of David Dale, the Bank's first agent in Glasgow, with the Bank
Arms in five colours in a panel at the right. The basic colour is blue but
there is a multicolour background. The back has a large illustration of the
Head Office. The £1 note, issued in the following year, is of the same
general design but in green and multicolour. The back illustrates the Head
Office and the chief office in Glasgow. It also incorporates magnetic
sorting marks. The portrait of David Dale is repeated in the watermark.
Both notes have steel strips.

1966–67
53   **One Pound**   D   Green and multicolour
     Printed signature of the General Manager.
     Printing: 1 Sep 1967
54   **Five Pounds**   z   Blue and multicolour
     Printed signatures of the General Manager and Chief Accountant.

A small number of "specimen" notes of most of the post-war issues were
prepared for distribution in banking circles.

*The Royal Bank of Scotland merged with the National Commercial Bank of Scotland
Ltd. in 1969 to form the Royal Bank of Scotland* Limited, *the notes of which must be
distinguished from the foregoing issues.*

53

The Royal Bank of Scotland Limited 1969–

In 1969 the National Commercial Bank of Scotland Ltd. and the Royal Bank of Scotland merged. These two banks together with their English subsidiaries Glyn Mills & Co., the National Bank Ltd. and Williams Deacon's Bank Ltd. combined to form the National & Commercial Banking Group Ltd. with headquarters in Edinburgh. The English banks then merged to become Williams & Glyn's Bank Ltd. while the Scottish banks formed the Royal Bank of Scotland *Limited*. This is now Scotland's largest bank with a note circulation (in March 1975) of £119,600,000.

The first notes were prepared by Bradbury Wilkinson & Co. Ltd. and were issued on 19 March 1969. The watermark is a profile portrait of David Dale and the notes have the now familiar steel strip. They bear the signatures of the two General Managers.

1969

1 **One Pound** D Green and multicolour
The Forth road bridge is the principal feature with the old railway bridge in the background. The back is engraved with the Arms of the Bank and has magnetic sorting marks.

2 **Five Pounds** z Blue and multicolour
The Arms of the Bank form the main feature and are contained in an oval panel at the left of the note. The back contains an engraving of Edinburgh Castle similar to that on the last type of National Commercial Bank £5 note, and has magnetic sorting marks.

3 **Ten Pounds** Y Brown and multicolour
Similar to the £5 note but the back illustrates the Tay road bridge with Dundee in the background.

4 **Twenty Pounds** x Purple and multicolour
Similar but back has an illustration of the Forth road bridge.

5 **One Hundred Pounds** x Red and multicolour
Similar.

The chief officer of the Bank having been designated Managing Director, new £1 and £5 notes were issued on 15 July 1970 bearing his signature in place of those of the two General Managers. The frame line of the £1 note was slightly modified to accommodate the change.

1970

6 **One Pound** D Green and multicolour
Similar to previous issue but with one signature only.

7 **Five Pounds** z Blue and multicolour
Similar.

A small number of "specimen" notes were prepared for distribution within banking circles. All are numbered A 000000.

On 4 January 1972 an entirely new series was issued featuring on the backs views of famous Scottish castles. The fronts of the notes are of uniform design with only slight modification for each denomination. This design consists of two circular panels that on the right containing the Bank's Arms while the corresponding panel on the left contains as a watermark a portrait of Adam Smith, the noted Scots economist. On the top left-hand corner is the emblem of the National & Commercial Banking Group appearing on notes for the first time. The notes were designed and engraved by Bradbury Wilkinson & Co. Ltd. and contain a steel strip. They have the printed signature of the Managing Director.

1972
 8   **One Pound**   D   Green and multicolour
      The back features Edinburgh Castle and has magnetic sorting marks.

 9   **Five Pounds**   z   Blue and multicolour
      The back features Culzean Castle in Ayrshire. Magnetic sorting marks.

6

8

THE ROYAL BANK OF SCOTLAND LTD. (contd.)

8 reverse

9 reverse

10 reverse

11 reverse

12 reverse

| 10 | **Ten Pounds** | Y | Brown and multicolour |

The back features Glamis Castle.

| 11 | **Twenty Pounds** | X | Purple and multicolour |

The back features Brodick Castle on the Isle of Arran.

| 12 | **One Hundred Pounds** | X | Red and multicolour |

The back features Balmoral Castle.

A small number of "specimen" notes of each value were prepared for restricted circulation. These bear serial number A 000000.

Printings of the £1 note

5 Jan 1972   2 Apr 1973

The Shetland Bank   1821–1842
Hay & Ogilvie

Hay & Ogilvie commenced business at Lerwick in 1821 and although they
designated themselves the Shetland Bank they were also engaged in trade.
They appear to have ceased to issue notes in 1827 but carried on until 1842,
when they failed with debts amounting to £60,000.

1821

1   **One Pound**   A   Black: uniface
    View of Lerwick flanked by "One Pound" on either side. Dated
    and numbered by hand. Three signatures. Engraved on steel by
    W. H. Lizars.

The Ship Bank   1750–1836
Colin Dunlop, Alexander Houston & Company 1750
Moores Carrick & Company 1777
Carrick, Brown & Company 1789

Founded by some of the prosperous tobacco lords of Glasgow in 1750, this
was one of the most famous of the old Scottish banks. It derived its name
from the fact that its notes had an illustration of a ship in full sail. Like the
Aberdeen Banking Company it soon incurred opposition from the Edinburgh banks but whereas the Aberdeen Company succumbed to the
pressure the Ship Bank, by virtue of its larger resources and the determina-
tion of its founders, survived. By 1761 the note circulation had reached a
figure of £82,331 later rising to £140,460 by 1823. In 1836 it amalgamated
with the Glasgow Bank Company to form the Glasgow and Ship Bank.

IN NAME OF COLIN DUNLOP, ALEXANDER HOUSTON & COMPANY

1754

1   **Twenty Shillings**   A   ·   Black: uniface
    Circular vignette (top left) of ship sailing towards the left. Payable
    on Demand. Dated and numbered by hand. Signed by the Cashier
    and by Colin Dunlop and Alexander Houston.

1759

2   **Twenty Shillings**   A   Black: uniface

Circular vignette (top left) of ship sailing towards the right. With Option Clause: "or in the option of the said company one pound and sixpence sterling at the end of six months after the day of the demand". Dated and numbered by hand. Signed by the Cashier and by Colin Dunlop and Alexander Houston. Watermark is a border of wavy lines.

1763

3   **One Pound**   A   Black: uniface

Circular vignette (top left) of ship sailing towards the right. Note headed "One Pound Sterling". Without Option Clause. Dated and numbered by hand. Signed by the Cashier and Colin Dunlop and George Oswald.

4   **Five Pounds**   W   Black: uniface

Circular vignette (top left) of ship sailing towards the right. "Five" in Gothic script "Pounds Ster" in copperplate script at top of the note. Dated and numbered by hand. Signed by the Cashier and by Colin Dunlop and Alexander Houston. Watermark border of wavy lines.

IN NAME OF CARRICK, BROWN & COMPANY

I

THE SHIP BANK (*contd.*)

1823

5   **One Guinea**   A   Black and blue: uniface
Circular vignette of ship (sailing towards the right in this and all
future issues) at top centre, flanked by a panel in blue containing
"One Guinea" at left and by "Glasgow" in black on the right. A
vertical panel in blue consists of intertwined initials. Dated and
numbered by hand and with a printed revenue stamp on the back.
Signed by the Cashier and two others.

1829

6   **Twenty Shillings**   A   Black and dull blue: uniface
Circular vignette of sailing ship at top left with a long oblong
panel in dull blue containing "Twenty Shillings" across the top of
the note. Vertical panel of initials in dull blue at the left. Dated and
numbered by hand. Signed by the Cashier and two others. Printed
revenue stamp on the back. Designed and engraved by Kirkwood
& Son.

Contemporary forgery known dated 3 March 1829.

1832

7   **Twenty Shillings**   A   Black: uniface
Central vignette of the Bank's Head Office flanked on each side by
engravings of ships under sail. Vertical panel at the left inscribed
"Ship Bank of Glasgow" and a horizontal panel across the centre

7

of the design inscribed "Carrick, Brown & Company, Bankers in Glasgow". Dated and numbered by hand and signed by the Cashier, the Accountant and one other. Designed and engraved on a steel plate by Joseph Swan, Glasgow.

Unissued notes endorsed in ink "Proof Note" exist.

The Southern Bank of Scotland 1838–1840

This short-lived bank opened at Dumfries on 11 June 1838 and quickly extended its influence by opening branches in seven neighbouring places. By 1840 the need for amalgamation had become apparent and negotiations were completed with the Edinburgh & Leith Bank. At this time the Southern Bank had deposits amounting to £75,000 and a note circulation of £20,000.

1838

1 **One Pound** A Black: uniface

Arms of Dumfries flanked on each side by "One Pound". Dated and numbered by hand and signed by the Manager and the Accountant. Designed and engraved on steel by W. & A. K. Johnston.

A proof of this note exists.

2 **Twenty Pounds** W
Similar.

STEWART BUCHANAN & COMPANY
See The Perth United Company.

JOHN STEWART & COMPANY
See the Perth United Company.

The Stirling Banking Company   1777–1826

This company was actually a continuation of a private bank established in 1777. It was badly managed and was sequestrated on 14 August 1826 with liabilities of £182,896, although Kerr estimates the figure at nearer a quarter of a million. The creditors were ultimately paid in full.

No details of the notes of the private bank appear to have been recorded, but bogus notes were issued in Stirling in 1784 signed by Robert Belch and James Drysdale. These had no connection with the Stirling Banking Company.

1808

1   **Five Pounds**   w   Black: uniface
Small circular vignette of a lamb flanked by "Five Pounds" and "Stirling". Numbered and dated by hand and signed by the Cashier and one other. Watermarked "The Stirling Banking Company". Engraved on a copper plate by Kirkwood & Son.

1810

2   **One Pound**   A   Black: uniface
Vignette of Stirling Castle flanked by "One Pound" and "Stirling". Dated and numbered by hand and signed by the Cashier and one other. Watermarked "One Pound Stirling". Designed and engraved on a copper plate by Kirkwood & Son.

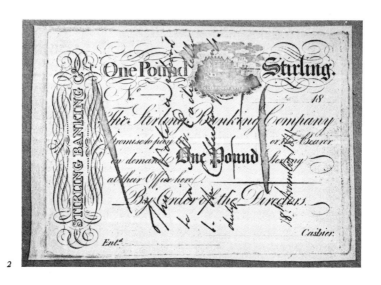

2

1817

  3 **One Guinea**   A   Black: uniface
      Oval vignette of Stirling Castle flanked by "One Guinea" and
      "Stirling". Dated and numbered by hand and signed by the
      Cashier and one other. Designed by Butterworth and engraved by
      Kirkwood & Son.

The Stirling Merchant Banking Company 1784–1813

Founded in 1784, the business was entirely a local one and in fact the bank
never enjoyed a good reputation. Its failure in 1813, however, was occasioned by a fraud on the part of one of the partners. The debts of
£50,104 were ultimately paid in full.

1799

  1 **One Guinea**   A   Black: uniface
      No vignette but "One Guinea" in large Gothic letters at the top of
      the note. Numbered by hand but with a printed date (2 August
      1799). Signed by the Cashier and one other. Engraved on a copper
      plate by Kirkwood & Son.

1801

  2 **One Pound**   A   Black: uniface
      Small vignette of the town of Stirling at top left. "One Pound" in a
      central position at the top. Dated and numbered by hand and
      signed by the Cashier and the Accountant. Engraved on a copper
      plate by Kirkwood & Son. Designed by G. Paton.

1800

  3 **Five Shillings**   110 × 90 mm.   Black: uniface
      Central vignette featuring a lamb flanked by "Five" and
      "Shillings". Printed date 1 January 1800 and numbered by hand.
      Signed by the Cashier and one other. Designed by G. Paton and
      engraved by Kirkwood & Son.

  4 **One Guinea**   A   Black: uniface
      Oval vignette of lamb flanked by "One" and "Guinea". Printed
      date 1 May 1800 and numbered by hand. Signed by the Cashier
      and one other. Designed by G. Paton and engraved by Kirkwood
      & Son. Watermarked "Stirling One Pound".

STORNOWAY or STORNAWAY "BANK"
See J. Stewart Mackenzie.

The Thistle Bank   1761–1836
Sir James Maxwell, James Ritchie & Company

Began business in November 1761 with a capital of £7,000, having been
founded in Glasgow by "tobacco lords" wishing to emulate the success of
the Ship Bank. The name was derived from the thistle emblem which
appeared on all its notes and these circulated throughout the country. The
bank pursued a more progressive policy than did its rival in consequence it
had more widely fluctuating profits. In 1836 it merged in the Glasgow
Union Banking Company.

ISSUED IN NAME OF SIR JAMES MAXWELL OF POLLOCK BART., JAMES
RITCHIE & COMPANY BANKERS IN GLASGOW AT THE THISTLE

1761
  1 **Twenty Shillings**   A   Black: uniface
     Vignette of thistle surrounded by a circular frame of leaves and
     flanked by "One Pound" and "Sterling", both in upper and
     lower-case letters. Dated and numbered by hand and signed by the
     Cashier and one other.

ISSUED IN NAME OF THE THISTLE BANK COMPANY

1799
  2 **Five Shillings** 120 × 95 mm.   Black and blue: uniface
     Small thistle emblem contained in an oval at top centre. "Five
     Shillings" in ornate letters above. Vertical panel of thistles at left.
     Printed date 2 December 1799 but numbered by hand. Signed on
     behalf of the Cashier. Engraved on a copper plate by Kirkwood &
     Son.

1813
  3 **One Pound**   A   Black: uniface
     Thistle emblem flanked by panels containing "One Pound" (left)
     and "£1 Glasgow" (right). Dated and numbered by hand. Signed
     by the Cashier and one other. Designed by Menzies and engraved
     by Kirkwood & Son.
     Contemporary forgery known dated 2 November 1813.

1

4   **One Guinea**   A   Black: uniface
      Thistle emblem flanked by panels containing "One" and
      "Guinea". Dated and numbered by hand. Vertical panel of thistles
      at left. Signed by the Cashier and one other. Designed by G. Paton
      and engraved by Kirkwood & Son.
      Contemporary forgery known dated 1 December 1813.

1820

5   **One Guinea**   A   Black: uniface
      Thistle emblem (broader than on previous designs) surmounted by
      "One Guinea" in a curved panel and flanked by "£1-1." and
      "Glasgow". Vertical panel of thistles at left. Payable to John
      Kemp. Dated and numbered by hand. Designed and engraved by
      Kirkwood & Son.

It is almost certain that notes of larger denomination were issued but no
records confirming this fact have been seen.

Andrew, George and Andrew Thomson 1785–1793
Messrs. Thomson

A small bank opened in 1785 at Glasgow by Andrew, George and Andrew
Thomson (a father and two sons), the younger son, Andrew, acting as

ANDREW, GEORGE and ANDREW THOMSON (contd.)

Cashier. It failed in 1793 with debts of £47,000 which were ultimately paid in full.

1785

1   **Twenty Shillings**   A   Black: uniface
     Shield of Arms at top left. "Twenty Shillings" in a panel of curves at the right. Vertical panel of roses at the left inscribed "Thomsons". Printed date 1 October 1785 and numbered by hand. Two signatures.

The Town & County Bank Limited   1825–1908
The Aberdeen Town & County Banking Company

Established as The Aberdeen Town & County Banking Company in 1825 with a capital of £750,000, it almost immediately opened a number of branches in the north-east. Limited Liability was adopted in 1882 and the title of the bank became the Town & County Bank Ltd. The authorised Circulation was £70,133 but by the end of the century the actual circulation had reached £300,000. On 1 May 1908 it merged with its Aberdeen rival, the North of Scotland Bank Ltd., to form the North of Scotland & Town & County Bank Limited. At this time it had 69 branches.

The first notes were printed from steel plates prepared by Perkins & Heath of London and were inscribed "The Aberdeen Town & County Banking Company". They were dated and numbered by hand and signed by the Cashier and the Secretary. They were made payable to John Smith, and bore a printed revenue stamp on the back.

1825

1   **One Pound**   A   Black: uniface
     Central vignette of a pillared building flanked by oval panels containing "One".

2   **Five Pounds**   W   Black: uniface
     "Five Pounds" in curved letters above the figure 5 in a wreath of oak leaves, all at top centre; flanked on the left with the building illustrated in the £1 note and on the right by a view of Union Street, Aberdeen.

3   **Ten Pounds**   W   Black: uniface
     Similar general design to that of the £5 note.

4   **Twenty Pounds**   W   Black: uniface
     Similar.

1862

5 **One Pound**   A   Black
Similar to the first £1 note but the back now has an engraving of Balmoral Castle with portraits of Queen Victoria and Prince Albert. The date is now printed (1 May 1862).

In 1862 the Bank was incorporated by Act of Parliament and a new series of notes was prepared to include reference to this. The design is more or less uniform for each denomination and features a view of Aberdeen from the south. The Head Office of the bank is illustrated on a panel at the left and the notes are signed on behalf of both the Manager and the Secretary. Engraved on steel by Perkins Bacon & Co. The dates and numbers are now printed.

1863

6 **One Pound**   A   Black: uniface
Payable to bearer.

7 **Five Pounds**   W
Similar.

8 **Ten Pounds**   W
Similar.

9 **Twenty Pounds**   W
Similar.

10 **One Hundred Pounds**   W
Similar.

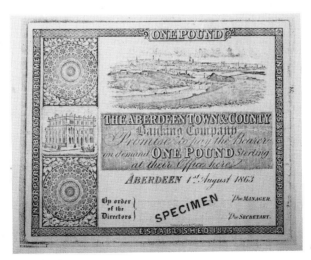

6

THE TOWN & COUNTY BANK LTD. (contd.)

In 1882 the Bank registered under the Companies Act of 1879 and the plates were altered to read "The Town and County Bank Limited". Lithographic panels in colour representing the value of each note were superimposed on the existing legend panels. Other details remain as before.

1882

11	**One Pound**	A	Black with panel of value in indigo
	Inscribed "The Town and County Bank, Limited".		
12	**Five Pounds**	W	Black and indigo: uniface
13	**Ten Pounds**	W	Brown with panel of value in green: uniface
14	**Twenty Pounds**	W	Blue and indigo: uniface
15	**One Hundred Pounds**	W	Blue and indigo: uniface

Specimen notes of most denominations exist.

After the merger with the North of Scotland Bank Ltd. existing notes were recirculated overprinted in red "The North of Scotland and Town & County Bank Limited in which is incorporated The Town & County Bank Limited".

II

The overprint (across centre value panel) reads "The North of Scotland and Town & County Bank Limited/in which is incorporated/The Town and County Bank Limited".

The Tweed Bank
Batson Berry & Company
Batson Berry & Langhorn

1813–1841

Strictly speaking this is an English private bank, but as the notes circulated most in the Scottish county of Berwickshire it is appropriate to include particulars of them here. There is some evidence that branches or agencies existed in Kelso and Selkirk.

Founded in Berwick-on-Tweed in 1813, it failed in 1841. Five dividends totalling 10s.3d. in the £ were paid to noteholders and a number of the notes have survived, no doubt in the hope of a sixth dividend.

1813

1 **One Pound**   A   Black: uniface
"Tweed Bank" at top between handwritten numbers. Dated by hand. Oval vignette of sailing vessel at the mouth of the River Tweed. Signed on behalf of the firm.

THE TWEED BANK (contd.)

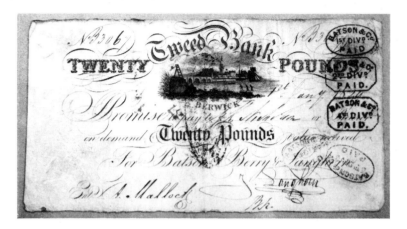

1818

2   **One Pound**   A   Black : uniface
     Vignette of the Mouth of the Tweed at top left. Dated and
     numbered by hand. Signed on behalf of the firm.

3   **Five Pounds**   W   Black : uniface
     Engraving of the town of Berwick and bridge over the River Tweed
     flanked on either side by "Tweed" and "Bank". Dated and
     numbered by hand. Engraved on steel by Perkins & Petch, London
     (later Perkins Bacon & Co.). Signed on behalf of the firm.

4   **Twenty Pounds**   W   Black : uniface
     Vignette of the Mouth of the Tweed flanked by "Twenty" and
     "Pounds". Dated and numbered by hand. Signed on behalf of the
     firm.

The Union Bank of Scotland   1843–1955
The Union Bank of Scotland Limited

It would be correct to state that this bank originated in 1830 with the
founding of the Glasgow Union Banking Company, the national title being
adopted in 1843. As its name suggests, the strength of the Union Bank
stems from the many old Scottish banking houses which it absorbed. These
(together with the date of absorption) were:

1836   The Thistle Bank

1838 Sir William Forbes, James Hunter & Co.
1838 The Paisley Union Bank
1843 The Glasgow & Ship Bank
    which included The Ship Bank
        The Glasgow Bank Company
1843 Hunters & Company
    which included Hunters & Co., Ayr
        The Kilmarnock Banking Company
1849 The Banking Company in Aberdeen
1857 The Perth Banking Company
    which included Six banking houses in Perth
        The Perth United Company

The bulk of its business was originally concentrated in the south-west of the country with its Head Office and Administration centred in Glasgow. It had, however, a second Head Office in Edinburgh and many of the notes are unique in that they are inscribed payable at either Glasgow or Edinburgh. The branch system eventually extended throughout the country.

On 3 April 1882 the Bank was registered as a limited liability company under the name of the Union Bank of Scotland Limited, the capital at that time being increased to £5 million. In 1955 a merger was arranged with the Bank of Scotland, the name of the senior bank being retained for the joint business.

The Authorised Circulation under the 1845 Act was £327,223 to which figure was added £88,467 in respect of the Banking Company in Aberdeen and £38,656 through the merger with the Perth Banking Company. The actual circulation at the time of the merger with the Bank of Scotland exceeded £10 million.

The variety and general excellence of design of the Union Bank notes provide collectors with an interesting field for specialisation. The early issues are of a complex nature and much of the detail in the following list has been gained from perusal of the notes and proofs held by the Bank of Scotland.

THE UNION BANK OF SCOTLAND

The first notes were printed from steel plates engraved by W. H. Lizars. All denominations have the names of four constituent banks incorporated in the border of the design. They are dated by hand but have printed numbers and have printed revenue stamps on the back. Signed on behalf of the Accountant and the Cashier.

1843
1 **One Pound**   A   Black: uniface
    Two equestrian statues at top left and right with "One Pound"

THE UNION BANK OF SCOTLAND *(contd.)*

between. Vignettes of female figures representing the Arts (lower left) and Commerce & Industry (lower right).

2 **Five Pounds** w Black: uniface
Similar general design but with differing vignettes in the lower portion of the note.

3 **Ten Pounds** w Black: uniface
Three allegorical figures at top centre flanked on each side by "Ten Pounds". Equestrian statues at lower left and right.

4 **Twenty Pounds** w Black: uniface
Frontal views of the two equestrian statues with figures "20" between, the whole vignette being flanked by "Twenty" and "Pounds". Allegorical figures at lower left and right.

5 **One Hundred Pounds** w Black: uniface
The central vignette consists of a small portrait of Queen Victoria supported by two female figures and flanked on each side by "£100". Frontal views of the two equestrian statues provide the lower vignettes.

The above notes are payable at Edinburgh, with the exception of the £100 note which is payable at Glasgow.

A proof in the collection of the Bank of Scotland consists of a £100 note of similar design to that listed but omitting the figures of value

I

which flank the vignette. This is payable at Edinburgh. The actual issue of a note of this description cannot be confirmed.

In 1846 the names of Hunters and Co. and the Glasgow & Ship Bank were added to those of the four banks surrounding the design, thus making six banks in all. Other details remained unchanged. The £20 note is payable in Glasgow and the remainder in Edinburgh.

1846

6	**One Pound**	A	Black: uniface
	Six banks listed on the borders.		
7	**Five Pounds**	W	Black: uniface
	Similar.		
8	**Ten Pounds**	W	Black: uniface
	Similar.		
9	**Twenty Pounds**	W	Black: uniface
	Similar.		
10	**One Hundred Pounds**	W	Black: uniface
	Similar.		

Around 1850 a new series of large-denomination notes was prepared by Perkins Bacon & Petch of London. The main feature of the design is the equestrian statue of William of Orange in the Trongate, Glasgow. This appears in a central position at the top flanked on each side by panels containing the value either in words or figures and differing in shape in each denomination. The design is otherwise uniform for the series. A vertical panel at the left contains the names of six constituent banks in oval formats. The backs are printed with a uniform design consisting of the title of the bank in a circular panel. The notes, made payable at Glasgow, are signed by or on behalf of the Accountant and the Cashier.

1850

11	**Five Pounds**	W	Black with printed back
12	**Ten Pounds**	W	
	Similar.		
13	**Twenty Pounds**	W	
	Similar.		
14	**One Hundred Pounds**	W	
	Similar.		

The Banking Company in Aberdeen was absorbed in 1849 and the plate for the £1 note was modified to include that name with the others in the sur-

THE UNION BANK OF SCOTLAND (contd.)

rounding borders. Seven banks are now so detailed. The remaining features are unaltered. Payable at Edinburgh.

1850

15   **One Pound**   A
    (*a*) Black: uniface.
    (*b*) Black but with small ornaments in red on each side of "One" (probably control marks): uniface.

Later the above note appeared with a printed back featuring the equestrian statue in blue.

1855

16   **One Pound**   A   Black; back printed in blue

In 1863 the Bank having registered under the Companies Act of the previous year adopted the full legal description "The Union Bank of Scotland, Incorporated under Act of Parliament". In consequence new designs were prepared for the £1 note and incorporating "Pursuant to Act of Parliament". This was also added to the existing £5 note.

1863

17   **One Pound**   A   Blue and green: uniface
    Arms of the Bank flanked by panels containing the value. A panel containing the word "One" in large letters is superimposed in green on the legend panel. Printed date and number and signed

15

on behalf of the Accountant and the Cashier. Payable in Glasgow *or* Edinburgh.

A dangerous forgery of this note is dated 1 November 1865.

18   **Five Pounds**   w   Black: uniface
"Pursuant to act of Parliament". This was printed from the old Lizars plate but now bears the imprint of W. & A. K. Johnston.

From 1863 all notes are made payable in both Glasgow and Edinburgh

In 1867 a completely new series was issued from steel plates engraved by Perkins and Bacon. All denominations have the same general design apart from variations in the panels of value. The Bank's Arms are featured in a central position at the top of the design, flanked by panels containing the value expressed in words in the £1 and £10 notes and in figures in the case of the others. The two equestrian statues of William of Orange and Charles II appear at the lower left and right of the design. All notes now have printed dates and numbers and are signed by or on behalf of the Accountant and the Cashier. The basic plates are printed in black but panels containing the words of value in large letters are superimposed in green on the legend panels. On the £100 note this is expressed in figures.

1867

19   **One Pound**   A   Black and green: uniface
       Plate A (1867)   Plate B (1871)
       Plate C (1874)   Plate D (1878)

20   **Five Pounds**   w   Black and green: uniface

21   **Ten Pounds**   w
       Similar.

22   **Twenty Pounds**   w
       Similar.

23   **One Hundred Pounds**   w
       Similar.

A new £100 note was issued in 1872 differing from the previous issue in having the Bank's title in curved lettering across the top of the design. The position of the vignettes containing the statues has been raised to accommodate an oblong panel at the left containing the words "One Hundred". Engraved by Perkins Bacon & Co.

1872

24   **One Hundred Pounds**   w   Black and red: uniface

THE UNION BANK OF SCOTLAND (*contd.*)

19

THE UNION BANK OF SCOTLAND LIMITED

In 1882 the Bank registered under the Companies act of 1879 adding "Limited" to its title. The existing plates were suitably modified and a new series printed in a bright shade of blue with panels containing the words of value (figures in the £100 note) superimposed on the legend panels in dark red. Signed on behalf of the Accountant and the Cashier but the £100 notes personally signed by these officials. During the currency of this issue "Ltd" was added to the printers' imprint.

21

1882

25	One Pound	A	Bright blue and dark red; back printed in blue
26	Five Pounds	W	
	Similar.		
27	Ten Pounds	W	
	Similar.		
28	Twenty Pounds	W	
	Similar.		
29	One Hundred Pounds	W	
	Similar.		

Plates for the £1 note

Plate A	15 Apr 1882	2 Jun 1884	
Plate B	4 Nov 1885	16 May 1887	1 Apr 1889
Plate C	6 Jul 1889	2 Apr 1891	
Plate D	19 Jul 1892	20 Jul 1893	
Plate E	7 Jul 1894	15 Jul 1895	
	2 Apr 1896		
Plate F	5 Mar 1897	18 Feb 1898	
	31 Jan 1899		
Plate G	28 Feb 1899	24 Oct 1900	
Plate H	13 Sep 1901	29 Aug 1902	

Commencing with the issue from Plate H dated 10 March 1903 the signature of the Accountant on the £1 notes was printed. Other denominations continued to be hand-signed.

1903

30	One Pound	A	Blue and red

As previous issue but with printed signature of the Accountant.

In 1905 the contract for producing the plates passed to Waterlow & Sons Ltd. and was held by that company for all future issues. The new designs are basically similar to those of the previous Perkins Bacon notes but with re-designed panels of value flanking the Bank's Arms. The colours are unchanged but the backs have been completely re-designed with elaborate engraving surrounding the circular panel containing the Bank's name and the value. These new designs with small modifications were to remain for twenty years in the case of the £1 notes and for over forty years in the case of the others. They may be said to herald the "modern" issues of this Bank which are more readily available to the collector. Printed signature of the Accountant on the £1 note but hand-signed on behalf of the Accountant

THE UNION BANK OF SCOTLAND (contd.)

and the Cashier on the other denominations. The £100 notes continued to be personally signed by the two officials.

1905

31	**One Pound**	A	Blue and red; back printed in blue
32	**Five Pounds** Similar.	W	
33	**Ten Pounds** Similar.	W	
34	**Twenty Pounds** Similar.	W	
35	**One Hundred Pounds** Similar.	W	

Recorded printings:

				Printed signature
£1	6 Apr 1905	27 Mar 1906	1 May 1907	J. R. Wood
	2 Jan 1908	28 Sept 1909		G. H. Moritz
	12 Feb 1910	9 Sep 1910	12 Apr 1912	
	20 Aug 1913			John Alexander
	3 Aug 1914	24 Dec 1914	8 Nov 1915	
	25 Feb 1916	25 Jul 1916	30 Mar 1917	
	4 Oct 1917	4 Apr 1918	20 Jun 1919	J. F. McCrindle
	28 Feb 1919	20 Jun 1919	7 Jul 1920	
	10 Dec 1920			

31

32

Serial letters F and G appear in Gothic and the remainder in Roman type.

Hand-signed

£5	25 Feb 1905	6 Oct 1909	17 Sep 1912	On behalf of
	1 Aug 1914	14 Jul 1916	3 Oct 1917	Accountant and
	20 Sep 1918	16 Jan 1920		Cashier
£10	4 Apr 1905	15 Oct 1913	23 Mar 1917	ditto
	28 Feb 1918			
£20	31 Mar 1905	8 Oct 1913	3 Nov 1915	ditto
	20 Sep 1917	26 Aug 1918	4 Jun 1920	
£100	27 Mar 1906	4 Nov 1913	9 Nov 1915	By Accountant and Cashier

In order to provide a greater measure of security the current series of notes were issued in 1921 with a lithographic overlay in the form of a "sunburst" and printed in orange and red, details of the basic plate remaining unchanged. Variations in the type and combination of signatures on notes of £5 and upwards took place during the long currency of this series and as noted below.

1921

36 **One Pound**   A   Blue, red and orange
    Printed signature of General Manager

37 **Five Pounds**   W
    Similar:
    (*a*) Printed signature of General Manager and hand-signed on behalf of the Cashier (1921).

THE UNION BANK OF SCOTLAND (contd.)

   (*b*) Printed signatures of General Manager and Chief Accountant (1928).

   (*c*) Printed signatures of General Manager and Cashier.

38 **Ten Pounds**   W
   Similar. Printed signatures of General Manager and Chief Accountant. This denomination had a very limited circulation.

39 **Twenty Pounds**   W
   Similar:
   (*a*) Hand-signed on behalf of the General Manager and the Chief Accountant.
   (*b*) Hand-signed on behalf of the General Manager and the Cashier (1937).
   (*c*) Printed signatures of the General Manager and the Cashier.

40 **One Hundred Pounds**   W
   Similar:
   (*a*) Hand-signed on behalf of the General Manager and the Cashier (1923 and again in 1939).
   (*b*) Hand-signed on behalf of the General Manager and the Chief Accountant (1931).
   (*c*) Printed signatures of the General Manager and the Cashier.

Recorded printings:

			Printed signatures
£1	1 Oct 1921	2 Nov 1923	N. L. Hird

£5	5 Apr 1921	5 Apr 1926	15 Jan 1927	N. L. Hird
	6 Jul 1928	5 Mar 1930	3 Oct 1931	N. L. Hird &
	4 May 1932			J. F. McCrindle
	2 Feb 1933	15 Dec 1933	3 Sept 1934	N. L. Hird &
	1 Nov 1935	18 May 1936		J. D. Wink
	18 Aug 1937	31 May 1938	10 Jul 1939	N. L. Hird &
	24 Jun 1940	29 Sep 1941	30 Apr 1942	W. J. Wilson
	4 Aug 1942	20 Oct 1942	30 Jan 1943	
	25 May 1943	24 Jul 1944	31 Aug 1944	
	12 Sep 1946			
	31 Mar 1947	10 Jun 1947	3 May 1949	J. A. Morrison & W. J. Wilson
£10	3 Aug 1923	4 Jul 1928		N. L. Hird & J. F. McCrindle
	8 Dec 1933	8 Jul 1935		N. L. Hird & J. D. Wink *Handsigned*
£20	2 Aug 1923	3 Jul 1928	2 Aug 1932	On behalf of General Manager & Chief Accountant
	5 Sep 1933	2 Oct 1934	14 Aug 1935	
	31 May 1937	30 Nov 1938	3 Jan 1939	On behalf of General Manager & Cashier
	1 Jun 1940	2 Jan 1942		
	1 Feb 1943	10 Jul 1944		*Printed signatures* N. L. Hird & W. J. Wilson
	2 Dec 1946	1 Sep 1947		J. A. Morrison & W. J. Wilson *Handsigned*
£100	1 Aug 1923			p. General Manager & p. Cashier
	16 Apr 1931	1 Dec 1933	20 May 1936	p. General Manager & p. Chief Accountant
	1 Mar 1939	2 Jan 1942		p. General Manager & p. Cashier
	18 Feb 1947			*Printed signatures* General Manager & Cashier.

On 2 June 1924 the £1 note was issued in reduced format, and these notes together with the £1 note of the North of Scotland Bank were the forerunners of similarly reduced notes of the other Scottish banks. The design of the new note retains many of the features of the old, but the title

THE UNION BANK OF SCOTLAND (contd.)

of the Bank is now boldly set across the centre of the note. The "sunburst" overlay is also retained. The design on the back consists of a large "£1" in the centre of a circular panel bearing the name of the Bank on the circumference. The plates were engraved by Waterlow & Sons Ltd. and the printed signatures are those of the General Manager and either the Cashier or the Chief Accountant.

1924

41 **One Pound**   B   Blue, red, orange and yellow. Reduced format

    (a) Printed signatures of General Manager and Cashier.

    (b) Printed signatures of General Manager and Chief Accountant.

Recorded printings:

			Printed signatures
2 Jun 1924	2 Oct 1924	4 Jan 1926	N. L. Hird & J. F. McCrindle as Cashier
3 Oct 1927			
2 Jan 1929	2 Apr 1930	3 Dec 1931	N. L. Hird & J. F. McCrindle as Chief Accountant
5 Dec 1931			
1 Jun 1933	17 Jun 1933	3 Oct 1934	N. L. Hird & J. D. Wink
31 Mar 1936			
12 Feb 1937	31 May 1938	10 Jul 1939	N. L. Hird & W. J. Wilson
1 Aug 1940	14 Jan 1942	28 Feb 1942	
10 Nov 1942	1 Jun 1943	10 Apr 1944	
28 Sep 1945			
20 Mar 1946	31 Jul 1946	1 Jun 1948	J. A. Morrison & W. J. Wilson

41(a)

42

New Arms were granted to the Bank by the Lord Lyon King of Arms in 1947 and an opportunity was then taken to prepare designs featuring them. The design is common to all denominations and consists of the new Arms at the left with the sailing ship emblem of the old Ship Bank at the right. The Bank's title appears across the top of the design and a "sunburst" overlay similar to that of the previous issue is retained. The back features an industrial and shipping scene underlying the Bank's close relations with Clydeside. One printed signature only, that of the General Manager, appears on notes of all denominations.

1949

42	**One Pound**	B	Blue, red, orange and yellow
43	**Five Pounds**	X	
	Similar. Now in reduced format.		
44	**Twenty Pounds**	X	
	Similar.		
45	**One Hundred Pounds**	X	
	Similar.		

43

THE UNION BANK OF SCOTLAND (contd.)

Recorded printings

				Printed signatures
£1	1 Mar 1949	17 Oct 1949	3 Jul 1950	J. A. Morrison
	2 Aug 1951	7 Apr 1952	6 Dec. 1952	
	1 Sept 1953			
	1 Jun 1954			Sir William Watson
£5	17 Jul 1950	5 Jun 1951	5 Feb 1952	J. A. Morrison
	3 Nov 1952	1 Oct 1953		
	2 Apr 1954			Sir William Watson
£20	1 Sept 1950	19 Jun 1951	6 May 1952	J. A. Morrison
	1 May 1953			
£100	9 Oct 1950	10 Mar 1952		J. A. Morrison
	1 Oct 1954			Sir William Watson

WEDDERSPOON & COMPANY
See the Perth United Company.

The Western Bank of Scotland   1832–1857

Commenced business at Glasgow in July 1832 with a paid-up capital of £209,170 held by 430 shareholders, and at the outset made remarkable progress, achieving this result according to Kerr "by setting at defiance the soundest principles of good management". By 1845 the capital had increased to £1,300,000 and the Ayrshire Banking Company was purchased. The Greenock Banking Company, the Dundee Union Bank and the Paisley Commercial Bank had also been taken over. As an inevitable result of the policies pursued difficulties arose in 1857 and matters were brought to a head on 9 November when the bank suspended payment. At this time the Western had 101 branches, a paid-up capital of £1½ million, deposits of £5,306,569 and its £50 shares stood on the market at £84. Public confidence had therefore been seriously misplaced in what Kerr referred to as an "insane bank". The total liabilities at the time of the stoppage amounted to £8,911,932. At first the other banks hesitated to accept Western notes but as this increased public panic, two days later they were accepted in the normal course. In 1870 the outstanding liabilities were assumed by the National Bank of Scotland on consideration of a payment of £8,448, that bank in consequence retiring any of the notes still outstanding. The Authorised Circulation was £337,938.

1832

1   **One Pound**   A   Black: uniface
Engraving of the Royal Exchange flanked by "One Pound" and "Glasgow". Vignettes at lower left and right represent "Prosperity" and "Britannia" respectively. Dated and numbered by hand and signed on behalf of the Manager and the Accountant. Printed revenue stamp on the back. Engraved on steel by Joseph Swan.

2   **Five Pounds**   W   Black: uniface
Royal Exchange flanked by "Five Pounds Glasgow" and "Five Pounds (date)". Vignettes representing Commerce and Britannia at middle left and right. Signed on behalf of the Manager and the Accountant and dated and numbered by hand. Printed revenue stamp on the back. Engraved on steel by W. H. Lizars.

3   **Ten Pounds**   W   Black: uniface
Three classical female figures representing Industry, the Arts and Commerce at top centre, surmounted by the bank's title in curved lettering. "Ten" at each of the top corners. Statues at left and right of the note. Dated and numbered by hand and signed by the Manager and the Accountant. Printed revenue stamp on the back.

4   **Twenty Pounds**   W   Black: uniface
Portrait of William IV between illustrations of the Royal Exchange and Glasgow Cathedral, the whole vignette being flanked by "Twenty" and "Pounds". Figures of Commerce and Britannia as in the £5 note. Dated and numbered by hand and with printed revenue stamp on the back. Signed by the Manager and the Accountant. Engraved on steel by W. H. Lizars.

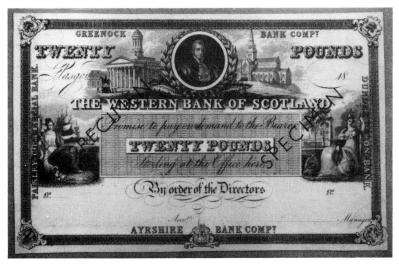

4

THE WESTERN BANK OF SCOTLAND (contd.)

5

5 **One Hundred Pounds**   w   Black: uniface
Portrait of William IV supported by the lion and unicorn of the
Royal Arms. "£100" on either side. Vignettes of Commerce and
Britannia at left and right. Dated and numbered by hand and
signed by the Manager and the Accountant. Printed revenue stamp
on the back. Engraved on steel by W. H. Lizars.

Around 1845 the plates were modified to include the names of the four
banks which had merged in the Western. These names are placed inside the
border of the large denominational notes and included within the border
on the £1 note. Other details are unaltered but printed numbers appeared
shortly after this new series was issued.

1845
6 **One Pound**   A   Black: uniface
Names of four banks inscribed inside each border.
(*a*) Numbered by hand.
(*b*) With printed number.

7 **Five Pounds**   w
Similar.

8 **Ten Pounds**   w
    Similar.

9 **Twenty Pounds**   w
    Similar.

10 **One Hundred Pounds** w
    Similar.

Proofs of most of the above notes exist.

Legislation

LEGISLATION AFFECTING THE ISSUE OF SCOTTISH BANKNOTES

1695 (Under the Scottish Parliament.) An "Act for erecting a Publick Bank" created the Bank of Scotland giving it a monopoly for 21 years.

1765 Option Clause prohibited, all notes after 15 May 1766 to be payable on demand.
No notes of lower denomination than £1 sterling to be issued on pain of a heavy fine.

1797 Issue of notes "for any sum whatever under the sum of 20s. sterling" permitted as a temporary measure because of the shortage of specie. This resulted in 5s. notes being issued by most banks.

1800 Stamp Duty levied on banknotes (see below).

1808 Licences to issue notes required (see below).

1826 Notes below £5 prohibited throughout England but efforts to extend this Act to Scotland prevented by the great strength of public opinion in that country.

1845 "An Act to Regulate the Issue of Bank Notes in Scotland". In effect an extension of Sir Robert Peel's English Bank Act of the previous year, it remains to this day the main regulator of Scottish issues. Among its many sections it

1. Established the "Authorised Circulation" of each bank based on the average circulation for the year to 1 May 1845.
2. Enabled banks in Scotland to issue in excess of the "Authorised" figure to the amount of gold and silver coin held.
3. Limited the issue of notes to those banks which had issued between 1 May 1844 and 1 May 1845 – in other words, no new bank of issue could now be established. Two banks of issue uniting in future could, however, retain both issues.
4. Notes for fractions of £1 sterling were prohibited.

1914 Scottish banknotes made legal tender. (No paper money had ever been legal tender in Scotland although Bank of England notes had been legal tender in England since 1833.) This clause was withdrawn on 1 January 1920 but Scottish notes were again accorded that status during the 1939–1945 war.

1928   Bank of England £1 and 10s. notes were made legal tender in Scotland. Scottish banks empowered to hold Bank of England notes in place of gold coin to cover excess issue over the Authorised Circulation figure. (Bank of England notes of £5 and upwards still not legal tender in Scotland.)

STAMP DUTY ON SCOTTISH NOTES

Prior to 1800 Scottish notes were untaxed but the Stamp Act of that year made them liable for duty at the following rates:

not exceeding £1 1s.	4d.
£2 2s.	8d.
£5 5s.	1s.
£20	1s. 6d.
£100	7s. 6d.

In 1815 the rates were increased as follows:

not exceeding £1	5d.
£2	10d.
£5	1s. 3d.
£10	1s. 9d.
£20	2s.
£100	8s. 6d.

Prior to 1815 the stamp was embossed on the face of each note but after that date it consisted of an ornate design in black and red on the back. The Bank of Scotland, the Royal Bank of Scotland and the British Linen Company, however, by various Acts of George III were permitted to issue their notes on unstamped paper, making themselves accountable to the Inland Revenue for the total stamp duty applicable to their circulation. In 1853 all the other banks were permitted to compound the duty and issue on unstamped paper at the rate of 8s. 4d. annually for every £100 issued. The stamp duty on Scottish banknotes was abolished in 1972.

LICENCES

Licences to issue notes were made necessary under the Act of 1808 and raised by a further Act of 1815 to £30 annually for each place or town where notes are issued. Where any bank has more than one branch in the same town they are all covered by the same licence. Licences were paid until 1971 but are not longer in force.

AUTHORISED CIRCULATIONS UNDER THE 1845 ACT

The year 1845 saw the passing of "An Act to Regulate the Issue of Bank Notes in Scotland". This important piece of legislation prohibited the setting-up of any new bank of issue. Banks already issuing notes could continue to do so without "cover" to the extent of their average circulation for the twelve months up to 1 May 1845. This figure is known as the *Authorised Circulation*. In contrast to the provisions of the similar English Act of 1844, which imposed a complete embargo on any excess issue by English banks over the Authorised Circulation figure, the total amount issued by Scottish banks was not restricted but any excess beyond the "authorised" limit had to be covered by an equivalent amount of gold and silver coin – later by Treasury and Bank of England notes

The Authorised Circulation was fixed as follows:

	£
Aberdeen Town & County Bank	70,133
Ayrshire Banking Company	53,656
Bank of Scotland	300,485
Banking Co. in Aberdeen	88,467
British Linen Company	438,024
Caledonian Banking Company	53,434
Central Bank of Scotland	42,933
City of Glasgow Bank	72,921
Clydesdale Banking Company	104,028
Commercial Bank of Scotland	374,880
Dundee Banking Company	33,451
Eastern Bank of Scotland	53,636
Edinburgh & Glasgow Bank	136,657
National Bank of Scotland	297,024
North of Scotland Bank	154,319
Perth Banking Company	38,656
Royal Bank of Scotland	183,000
Union Bank of Scotland	327,223
Western Bank of Scotland	284,282

Since 1845 three issues have lapsed, those of the Western, the Ayrshire and the City of Glasgow Banks. Through mergers, the others have been combined in the figures applicable to the present three banks.

	Authorised Circulation	Actual Circulation (March 1975)
Bank of Scotland	£1,289,222	£93,800,000
The Royal Bank of Scotland Ltd.	888,355	119,600,000
Clydesdale Bank Limited	518,753	39,900,000

It will be seen how the Authorised Circulation now bears little relation to the actual circulation, which now exceeds £250 million.

Bibliography

Although this is the first publication to deal specifically with the entire range of Scottish bank issues there are numerous works of an historical nature which collectors will find invaluable for a proper background appreciation of their particular field of interest.

Two works, both regrettably out of print and rapidly becoming collector's items in their own right, cannot be too strongly recommended. They are:

The History of Banking in Scotland by Andrew W. Kerr first published by A. & C. Black Ltd., London, in 1884 and brought up to date in several later editions.

The One Pound Note in Scotland by William Graham, published by James Thin, Edinburgh, in 1886 with a second edition in 1911. This is an historical review of the importance of the £1 note in the Scottish economy and illustrates some of the older notes.

While the present book was in the press a volume was published which should remain the standard textbook on Scottish banking history for many years to come. This is:

Scottish Banking: A History 1695–1973 by Professor S. G. Checkland published in 1975 by Collins of Glasgow and London at £8.25.

This important work of 785 pages can be regarded by collectors of Scottish banknotes as an invaluable investment.

The undernoted works contain full accounts of the history of the individual banks. Most were printed in limited editions for private circulation and again have attained the status of collectors' items. Copies may, however, be obtainable at local public libraries. Although references to the note issues are all too sparse the history of each bank will add much to a collector's interest in the notes in his possession.

BANK OF SCOTLAND
    The Bank of Scotland 1695–1945 by Charles A. Malcolm. Published by the
    Bank and printed by R. & R. Clark Ltd., Edinburgh. 1945.
BRITISH LINEN BANK
    The History of the British Linen Bank by Charles A. Malcolm. Edinburgh:
    T. & A. Constable Ltd., 1950.

CLYDESDALE BANK LTD.
The History of the Clydesdale Bank by J. M. Reid. Glasgow: Blackie & Son Ltd., 1938.

COMMERCIAL BANK OF SCOTLAND LTD.
The Story of the Commercial Bank of Scotland Ltd. 1810–1910 by James L. Anderson. Published in Edinburgh, 1910.
Our Bank. Edinburgh: Thomas Nelson & Sons Ltd. First edn., 1941; second edn., 1946.

DUNDEE BANKING COMPANY
A Century of Banking in Dundee by C. W. Boase. Edinburgh: R. Grant & Son, 1867.

SIR WILLIAM FORBES, JAMES HUNTER & COMPANY
Memoirs of a Banking-house by Sir William Forbes. Edinburgh: W. & R. Chambers, 1859.

GLASGOW (EARLY BANKS)
Glasgow Banking in Olden Times by John Buchanan. Glasgow: David Robertson & Co., 1884.

NORTH OF SCOTLAND BANK LTD.
The North of Scotland Bank 1836–1936 by Alexander Keith. Aberdeen: Aberdeen Journals Ltd., 1936.

ROYAL BANK OF SCOTLAND
The History of the Royal Bank of Scotland 1727–1927 by Neil Munro. Published by the Bank and printed by R. & R. Clark Ltd., Edinburgh, 1928.

UNION BANK OF SCOTLAND LTD.
The History of the Union of Scotland by Robert S. Rait. Glasgow: John Smith & Son (Glasgow) Ltd., 1930.

A small but useful volume entitled *The Bank Note Circulation of Scotland* by William Graham was published by C. & R. Anderson, Edinburgh, in 1926. This gives a résumé of the system combined with a description of the Note Exchange.

The files of the *Scottish Bankers Magazine* (The Institute of Bankers in Scotland) include many useful articles and paragraphs which provide background interest to late nineteenth and current century issues.

Valuation Guide

DEGREES OF RARITY OF SCOTTISH BANKNOTES

degree reference		Premium range above face (Rough Guide)	Grade
[1]	Current issue in circulation	—	
[2]	Former issue, but still circulating	—	
[3]	Obsolete issue but occasionally found in circulation	£5–£10	(EF)
[4]	No longer found in circulation but fairly readily available from dealers	£8–£15	(EF)
[5]	Small numbers in dealers' and collectors' hands. Not readily available	£20–£40	(VF)
[6]	Scarce. Only occasionally offered	£40–£70	(VF)
[7]	Very scarce. Very rarely offered	£70–£100	(VF)
[8]	Rare. Fewer than 50 known	£100–£150	(F)
[9]	Very rare. Fewer than 20 known	£150–£300	(F)
[10]	Of extreme rarity. Fewer than 10 known	from £250	(F)

These valuations refer to notes as issued. Proof and "specimen" notes of nineteenth century issues have survived in greater numbers and are generally worth less; but these are the only types likely to be available to collectors because of the extreme rarity of most of the issued notes.

In contrast, modern "specimen" and proof notes are produced in very small quantities and are seldom, if ever, seen on the market.

PRICES

The degrees of rarity have been compiled by the author with reference to known collections in institutional and private hands. The corresponding valuations shown above have, however, been supplied by Stanley Gibbons Currency Ltd.

(Except where otherwise stated, these refer to notes in issued form.)

Cat. No.	Denomination	Rarity
Aberdeen Banking Co. (1)		
1	20s.	(10)
2	£10	(10)
Aberdeen Banking Co. (2)		
1	£10	(10)
2	£1	(9)
3	£1	(9)
4	£1	(9)
5	£20	(10)
6	£1 1s.	(9)
7	£5	(10)
8	£20	(10)
9	5s	(9)
10	£20	(10)
11	£1	(9)
12	£1	(8)
13	£5	(9)
14	£20	(10)
Aberdeen Commercial Banking Company		
1	£1	(9)
2	£1	(9)
Arbroath Banking Company		
1	£1	(10)
2	£1	(10)
3	£5	(10)
4	£20	(10)
Ayrshire Banking Company		
1	£1	(10)

Cat. No.	Denomination	Rarity
Bank of Scotland		
1 to 36 incl.		(10)
37	£1	(9)
38	£1 1s.	(9)
39	£5	(10)
40	£10	(10)
41	£20	(10)
42	£1	(8)
43	£1 1s.	(8)
44	£2	(10)
45	£2 2s.	(10)
46	£5	(10)
47	£10	(10)
48	£20	(10)
49	£1 1s.	(9)
50	£5	(10)
51	£5	(10)
52(a)	£1	(9)
52(b)	£1	(8)
52(c)	£1	(8)
53	£10	(10)
54	£20	(10)
55	£100	(10)
56(a)	£5	(10)
56(b)	£5	(10)
57	£1	(8)
58	£5	(9)
59	£10	(9)
60	£20	(10)
61	£100	(10)
62	£1 Proof	(10)
63	£100 Proof	(10)
64	£100 Proof	(10)
65	£1	(8)
66	£5	(9)
67	£10	(10)
68	£20	(10)
69	£100	(10)
70	£100 Proof	(8)
71	£1	(8)
72	£5	(9)

Cat. No.	Denomination	Rarity		Cat. No.	Denomination	Rarity
73	£10	(10)		107	£100	(1)
74	£20	(10)		108	£10	(1)
75	£100	(10)				
76(a)	£1	(6)		**Bannockburn Iron Works**		
76(b)	£1	(5)				
77(a)	£5	(8)		1	£1	(7)
77(b)	£5	(5)				
78(a)	£10	(8)		**John Belsh & Company**		
78(b)	£10	(7)				
79(a)	£20	(8)		1	5s	(8)
79(b)	£20	(5)				
80(a)	£100	(10)		**The British Linen Bank**		
80(b)	£100	(9)		1–12 incl.		(10)
81	£1	(4)		13	£1 1s.	(8)
82	£5	(5)		14	20s	(8)
83	£10	(6)		15	£1 1s.	(8)
84	£20	(6)		16	20s	(8)
85	£100	(7)		17	£1 1s.	(8)
86	£1	(3)		18	£5	(9)
87	£5	(5)		19	£20	(10)
88(a)	£10	(6)		20	£100	(10)
88(b)	£10	(5)		21	£1	(8)
89(a)	£20	(5)		22	£1 1s.	(8)
89(b)	£20	(5)		23	£5	(8)
90(a)	£100	(7)		24	£10	(9)
90(b)	£100	(6)		25	£20	(9)
91(a)	£1	(3)		26	£100	(10)
91(b)	£1	(3)		27	£1	(7)
92	£5	(6)		28	£5	(8)
93	£5	(4)		29	£10	(8)
94	£1	(3)		30	£20	(9)
95	£5	(3)		31	£100	(10)
96	£1	(3)		32	£1	(8)
97	£5	(3)		33	£5	(8)
98(a)	£1	(3)		34	£10	(8)
98(b)	£1	(3)		35	£20	(9)
99	£5	(3)		36	£100	(10)
100	£20	(6)		37	£1	(8)
101	£100	(6)		38	£5	(8)
102	£1	(2)		39	£10	(10)
103	£5	(2)		40	£20	(10)
104	£1	(1)		41	£100	(10)
105	£5	(1)		42(a)	£1	(7)
106	£20	(1)		42(b)	£1	(6)

Cat. No.	Denomination	Rarity
The British Linen Bank (contd.)		
43	£5	(7)
44	£10	(8)
45	£20	(8)
46	£100	(10)
47	£1	(5)
48	£5	(6)
49	£10	(6)
50	£20	(8)
51	£100	(9)
52	£1	(5)
53(a)	£1	(4)
53(b)	£1	(4)
54(a)	£5	(5)
54(b)	£5	(4)
55(a)	£10	(6)
55(b)	£10	(6)
56(a)	£20	(6)
56(b)	£20	(5)
57(a)	£100	(7)
57(b)	£100	(6)
58	£5	(5)
59	£1	(4)
60	£5	(7)
61	£20	(6)
62	£100	(8)
63	£1	(4)
64	£5	(5)
65	£1	(5)
66	£1	(3)
67	£5	(3)

Caithness Banking Company

Cat. No.	Denomination	Rarity
1	£1	(10)
2	£1 1s.	(10)

The Caledonian Banking Co. Ltd.

Cat. No.	Denomination	Rarity
1	£1	(8)
2	£5	(8)
3	£10	(9)

Cat. No.	Denomination	Rarity
4	£20	(9)
5	£100	(10)
6	£1	(8)
7	£5	(8)
8	£10	(9)
9	£20	(10)
10	£100	(10)
11	£5	(8)
12	£1	(6)
13	£5	(8)
14	£10	(8)
15	£20	(9)
16	£100	(10)
17	£1	(6)
18	£5	(7)
19	£10	(8)
20	£20	(9)
21	£100	(10)

The Carron Company

Cat. No.	Denomination	Rarity
1	5s.	(8)

The Central Bank of Scotland

Cat. No.	Denomination	Rarity
1	£1	(8)
2	£5	(9)
3	£10	(9)
4	£20	(10)
5	£1	(8)
6	£1	(8)
7	£5	(9)
8	£10	(9)
9	£20	(10)

The City Banking Co. of Glasgow

Cat. No.	Denomination	Rarity
1	£1 Proof	(10)
2	£1 Proof	(10)
3	£5 Proof	(10)

Cat. No.	Denomination	Rarity
The City of Glasgow Bank		
1	£1	(8)
2	£1	(7)
3	£5	(8)
4	£20	(9)
5	£100	(10)
6	£1	(7)
7	£20	(9)
8	£5	(8)
9	£100	(10)
10	£1	(10)
11	£1	(7)
12	£1	(7)
13	£5	(9)
Clydesdale Bank Limited		
1	£1	(9)
2	£5	(9)
3	£10	(10)
4	£20	(10)
5	£100	(10)
6	£1	(8)
7	£5	(9)
8	£20	(9)
9	£100	(10)
10	£1	(8)
11	£1	(6)
12	£5	(7)
13	£20	(8)
14	£100	(10)
15	£1	(6)
16(a)	£5	(7)
16(b)	£5	(7)
17(a)	£20	(8)
17(b)	£20	(8)
18(a)	£100	(10)
18(b)	£100	(10)
19(a)	£1	(5)
19(b)	£1	(5)
19(c)	£1	(5)
20	£5	(5)
21	£1	(4)
22	£5	(5)

Cat. No.	Denomination	Rarity
23	£20	(6)
24	£100	(7)
25(a)	£1	(5)
25(b)	£1	(4)
26	£5	(4)
27(a)	£1	(3)
27(b)	£1	(3)
28	£5	(3)
29	£10	(4)
30	£20	(4)
31	£100	(6)
32	£1	(1)
33	£5	(1)
34	£10	(1)
35	£20	(1)
36	£100	(1)
The Commercial Bank of Scotland Limited		
1	£1	(10)
2	£5	(10)
3	£20	(10)
4	£100	(10)
5	£1 1s.	(9)
6(a)	£1	(9)
6(b)	£1	(9)
6(c)	£1	(9)
7	£5	(10)
8	£20	(10)
9	£100	(10)
10	£1	(10)
11	£1	(9)
12(a)	£1	(9)
12(b)	£1	(9)
12(c)	£1	(9)
13	£5	(10)
14	£10	(10)
15	£1	(9)
16	£1	(8)
17	£5	(9)
18	£10	(9)
19	£20	(9)
20	£100	(10)

Cat. No.	Denomination	Rarity
The Commercial Bank of Scotland (contd.)		
21	£1	(8)
22	£5	(9)
23	£10	(9)
24	£20	(9)
25	£100	(10)
26	£1	(8)
27	£5	(8)
28	£10	(9)
29	£20	(9)
30	£100	(10)
31(a)	£1	(10)
31(b)	£1	(8)
32	£5	(8)
33	£10	(9)
34	£20	(9)
35	£100	(10)
36(a)	£1	(7)
36(b)	£1	(7)
37	£5	(8)
38	£20	(9)
39	£100	(10)
40	£1	(8)
41	£5	(9)
42	£20	(10)
43	£100	(10)
44(a)	£1	(5)
44(b)	£1	(5)
44(c)	£1	(5)
44(d)	£1	(5)
45	£5	(6)
46	£20	(7)
47	£100	(10)
48	£1	(5)
49(a)	£5	(7)
49(b)	£5	(6)
50	£20	(7)
51	£100	(9)
52(a)	£1	(5)
52(b)	£1	(4)
52(c)	£1	(4)
52(d)	£1	(4)

Cat. No.	Denomination	Rarity
53	£1	(4)
54	£1	(4)
55	£5	(4)
56	£20	(6)
57	£100	(8)
Company of Bank of Aberdeen		
1	£1 1s.	(9)
John Craw & Company		
1	20s.	(10)
The Cupar Banking Company		
1	20s.	(9)
Douglas Heron & Company		
1	£1	(10)
2	£1 1s.	(10)
The Dumfries Bank		
1	£1	(10)
2	£5	(10)
3	£20	(10)
The Dumfries Commercial Bank		
1	£1 1s.	(6)
2	£1 1s.	(6)
3	£5	(7)
4	£1 1s.	(9)
The Dundee Banking Company		
1	5s.	(10)
2	10s.	(10)
3	£1	(10)
4	£5	(10)
5	£1	(10)
6	£5	(10)
7	£1	(9)
8	£5	(10)
9	£1	(9)

Cat. No.	Denomination	Rarity
10	£5	(10)
11	5s.	(9)
12	£1 1s.	(9)
13	£20	(10)
14	£1	(7)
15	£5	(9)
16	£20	(10)
17	£1	(8)
18	£5	(9)
19	£20	(10)
20	£100 Proof	(10)

The Dundee Commercial Bank (1)

1	20s.	(10)
2	5s.	(10)

The Dundee Commercial Bank (2)

1	£1	(8)

The Dundee New Bank

1	£1	(10)
2	£5	(10)

The Dundee Union Bank

1	20s.	(9)
2	£1	(9)
3	£1	(9)

East Lothian Banking Company

1	£1 1s.	(8)
2	£1	(4)
3	£5	(5)

The Eastern Bank of Scotland

1	£1	(9)
2	£5	(9)
3	£10	(10)
4	£20	(10)

Cat. No.	Denomination	Rarity
5	£1	(8)
6	£5	(9)
7	£1	(9)

The Edinburgh & Glasgow Bank

1	£1	(9)
2	£5	(9)
3	£10	(10)
4	£5	(9)

The Edinburgh & Leith Bank

1	£1	(9)
2	£1 1s.	(9)
3	£5	(9)
4	£10	(9)
5	£20	(10)
6	£100	(10)

Falkirk Banking Company

1	£1	(9)
2	5s.	(9)

The Falkirk Union Bank

1	20s.	(8)
2	£1 1s.	(8)
3	£5	(9)
4	£20	(9)

The Fife Banking Company

1	£1	(9)

Sir William Forbes, James Hunter & Company

1	£1 1s.	(9)
2	£5	(9)
3	20s.	(8)
4	£5	(9)
5	£1	(8)
6	£1 1s.	(8)

Cat. No.	Denomination	Rarity
The Galloway Banking Co.		
1	£1	(8)
2	£5	(8)
3	£1 1s.	(8)
Glasgow and Ship Bank		
1	£1	(9)
2	£5	(9)
3	£20	(10)
4	£100	(10)
The Glasgow Arms Bank		
1	20s.	(10)
2	£1 1s.	(9)
The Glasgow Bank Company		
1	£1	(9)
2	£1	(9)
3	£1	(9)
Glasgow Joint Stock Bank		
1	£1	(10)
Glasgow Union Banking Co.		
1	£1	(9)
2	£5	(9)
3	£20	(10)
The Greenock Bank Company		
1	£1 1s.	(8)
2	£5	(8)
3	£20	(8)
4	£1	(8)
5	£1	(8)
The Greenock Union Bank		
1	£1	(10)
2	£5	(10)

Cat. No.	Denomination	Rarity
Hunters and Company		
1	£1 1s.	(10)
2	£5	(10)
3	£1	(9)
Inglis Borthwick Gilchrist & Company		
1	£1	(9)
2	£1 1s.	(9)
George Keller & Company		
1	5s.	(6)
2	10s.	(6)
3	20s.	(6)
The Kilmarnock Bank		
1	£1 1s.	(10)
2	£2 2s.	(10)
Leith Banking Company		
1	20s.	(9)
2	£1 1s.	(9)
3	£2	(9)
4	£20	(8)
5(a)	£1 1s.	(8)
5(b)	£1 1s.	(7)
6(a)	20s.	(6)
6(b)	20s.	(5)
7	£1 1s.	(5)
8	£5	(7)
John Maberly & Company		
1	£1	(9)
2	£1	(7)
3	£1	(7)
4	£1	(7)
John McAdam & Company		
1	5s.	(10)
2	10s.	(10)

Cat. No.	Denomination	Rarity
J. S. Mackenzie—Stornoway		
1	£1 unused	(4)
Merchant Bank, Glasgow		
1	£1	(9)
The Montrose Bank		
1	£1	(9)
2	£1 1s.	(9)
3	£5	(9)
The National Bank of Scotland Ltd.		
1–11 incl.		(10)
12	£1	(8)
13	£5	(9)
14	£20	(10)
15	£100	(10)
16(a)	£1	(8)
16(b)	£1	(7)
17	£5	(8)
18	£20	(9)
19	£100	(10)
20	£1	(8)
21	£5	(8)
22	£20	(9)
23	£100	(9)
24	£1	(5)
25	£5	(5)
26	£20	(8)
27	£100	(9)
28	£1	(5)
29	£5	(5)
30	£20	(8)
31	£100	(9)
32	£1	(6)
33	£1	(4)
34	£1	(4)
35	£5	(5)
36	£20	(6)
37	£100	(8)

Cat. No.	Denomination	Rarity
38(a)	£1	(4)
38(b)	£1	(4)
39	£5	(5)
40	£20	(7)
41	£100	(8)
National Commercial Bank of Scotland Limited		
1	£1	(4)
2	£5	(5)
3	£20	(6)
4	£100	(7)
5	£5	(6)
6(a)	£1	(3)
6(b)	£1	(3)
7	£5	(4)
8	£10	(5)
9	£1	(4)
The North British Bank		
1	£1 Proof	(9)
2	£5 Proof	(9)
3	£20 Proof	(9)
4	£100 Proof	(10)
5	£5 Reprint	(5)
The North of Scotland Bank Ltd.		
1	£1	(9)
2	£5	(9)
3	£20	(10)
4(a)	£5	(8)
4(b)	£5	(8)
5	£1	(8)
6	£5	(8)
7	£20	(9)
8	£100	(10)
9	£1	(8)
10	£1	(8)
11	£5	(8)
12	£10	(9)
13	£20	(9)
14	£100	(10)

Cat. No.	Denomination	Rarity
The North of Scotland Bank Ltd. (contd.)		
15(a)	£1	(5)
15(b)	£1	(5)
15(c)	£1	(5)
16(a)	£5	(6)
16(b)	£5	(6)
17	£20	(8)
18	£100	(10)
19(a)	£1	(6)
19(b)	£1	(6)
20	£5	(6)
21	£20	(8)
22	£100	(10)
23	£1	(6)
24	£5	(6)
25	£20	(8)
26	£100	(10)
27	£1	(6)
28	£1	(5)
29	£5	(6)
30	£1	(4)
31	£5	(5)
32	£20	(7)
33	£100	(8)

The Paisley Banking Company

1	20s.	(10)
2	£5	(9)
3	£1	(8)
4	£1 1s.	(8)

The Paisley Commercial Bank

1	£1	(9)
2	£5	(9)
3	£20	(10)

The Paisley Union Bank

1	£1 1s.	(10)
2	£5	(10)
3	£1 1s.	(9)
4	£1	(9)

Cat. No.	Denomination	Rarity
Perth Banking Company		
1	£1 1s.	(9)
2	£5	(9)
3	5s.	(9)
4	20s.	(8)
5	£1 1s.	(8)
6	£5	(8)
7	£10	(9)
8	£20	(10)
9	20s.	(8)
10	20s.	(8)
11	£1	(8)
12	£5	(8)
13	£20	(10)
14	£1	(8)
15	£5	(8)
16	£20	(9)
17	£1	(8)
18	£5	(8)

Perth Union Bank

1	£1	(10)

Perth United Company

All notes		(10)

Ramsays Bonars & Co.

1	5s.	(10)
2	£10	(9)
3	£20	(10)

The Renfrewshire Banking Company

1	£1	(9)
2	£1 1s.	(9)
3	£1	(6)
4	£5	(7)

R. Robertson & Company

1	5s.	(9)

Cat. No.	Denomination	Rarity
The Royal Bank of Scotland		
1–12 incl.		(10)
13	£1 1s.	(8)
14	£5	(9)
15	£10	(10)
16	£20	(10)
17	£100	(10)
18	20s.	(9)
19	5s.	(9)
20	£1 1s.	(9)
21	£1	(8)
22(a)	£1	(7)
22(b)	£1	(7)
23	£1 1s.	(8)
24	20s.	(8)
25	£1 1s.	(8)
26	£5	(8)
27	£10	(9)
28	£20	(10)
29	£100	(10)
30(a)	20s.	(8)
30(b)	20s.	(8)
31	£1	(8)
32	£5	(8)
33	£10	(8)
34	£20	(9)
35	£100	(10)
36	£1	(8)
37	£5	(8)
38	£10	(9)
39	£20	(9)
40	£100	(10)
41	£1	(8)
42(a)	£5	(8)
42(b)	£5	(5)
42(c)	£5	(5)
42(d)	£5	(5)
43(a)	£10	(10)
43(b)	£10	(7)
44(a)	£20	(8)
44(b)	£20	(6)
44(c)	£20	(6)
44(d)	£20	(5)

Cat. No.	Denomination	Rarity
45(a)	£100	(8)
45(b)	£100	(8)
45(c)	£100	(8)
46(a)	£1	(8)
46(b)	£1	(8)
46(c)	£1	(7)
46(d)	£1	(5)
46(e)	£1	(5)
47	£1	(5)
48(a)	£1	(4)
48(b)	£1	(4)
48(c)	£1	(4)
48(d)	£1	(4)
49	£1	(4)
50(a)	£5	(4)
50(b)	£5	(5)
51	£1	(3)
52	£5	(4)
53	£1	(3)
54	£5	(3)
The Royal Bank of Scotland Limited		
1	£1	(3)
2	£5	(3)
3	£10	(4)
4	£20	(5)
5	£100	(6)
6	£1	(2)
7	£5	(2)
8	£1	(1)
9	£5	(1)
10	£10	(1)
11	£20	(1)
12	£100	(1)
The Shetland Bank		
1	£1	(8)
The Ship Bank		
1	20s.	(10)
2	20s.	(10)

Cat. No.	Denomination	Rarity
The Ship Bank (contd.)		
3	£1	(10)
4	£5	(10)
5	£1 1s.	(8)
6	20s.	(8)
7	20s.	(8)
The Southern Bank of Scotland		
1	£1	(9)
2	£20	(10)
The Stirling Banking Company		
1	£5	(9)
2	£1	(9)
3	£1 1s.	(9)
The Stirling Merchant Bank		
1	£1 1s.	(9)
2	£1	(9)
3	5s.	(9)
4	£1 1s.	(9)
The Thistle Bank		
1	20s.	(10)
2	5s.	(9)
3	£1	(9)
4	£1 1s.	(8)
5	£1 1s.	(9)
Andrew & George Thomson		
1	20s.	(10)
The Town & County Bank Ltd.		
1	£1	(9)
2	£5	(9)
3	£10	(10)
4	£20	(10)
5	£1	(9)

Cat. No.	Denomination	Rarity
6	£1	(8)
7	£5	(8)
8	£10	(9)
9	£20	(9)
10	£100	(10)
11	£1	(7)
12	£5	(8)
13	£10	(8)
14	£20	(9)
15	£100	(10)
The Tweed Bank		
1	£1	(7)
2	£1	(7)
3	£5	(6)
4	£20	(6)
The Union Bank of Scotland Limited		
1–15 incl.		(10)
16	£1	(9)
17	£1	(9)
18	£5	(10)
19	£1	(8)
20	£5	(9)
21	£10	(10)
22	£20	(10)
23	£100	(10)
24	£100	(10)
25	£1	(8)
26	£5	(9)
27	£10	(10)
28	£20	(10)
29	£100	(10)
30	£1	(8)
31	£1	(6)
32	£5	(7)
33	£10	(9)
34	£20	(9)
35	£100	(10)
36	£1	(6)
37(a)	£5	(6)
37(b)	£5	(5)

Cat. No.	Denomination	Rarity	Cat. No.	Denomination	Rarity
37(c)	£5	(5)	The Western Bank of Scotland		
38	£10	(7)	1	£1	(8)
39(a)	£20	(7)	2	£5	(8)
39(b)	£20	(6)	3	£10	(9)
39(c)	£20	(6)	4	£20	(9)
40(a)	£100	(9)	5	£100	(10)
40(b)	£100	(9)	6(a)	£1	(6)
40(c)	£100	(9)	6(b)	£1	(6)
41(a)	£1	(4)	7	£5	(7)
41(b)	£1	(4)	8	£10	(8)
42	£1	(4)	9	£20	(9)
43	£5	(5)	10	£100	(10)
44	£20	(6)			
45	£100	(8)			